PLAY FREE

CHANGE THE GAME

DR. RICHIE SARLO

Play Free: Change the Game

Trilogy Christian Publishers A Wholly Owned Subsidiary of Trinity Broadcasting Network
2442 Michelle Drive Tustin, CA 92780

Cover design by: Trilogy
For information about special discounts for bulk purchases, please contact Trilogy Christian Publishing.

Manufactured in the United States of America
10 9 8 7 6 5 4 3 2 1
Library of Congress Cataloging-in-Publication Data is available.
ISBN: 978-1-68556-807-8
E-ISBN: 978-1-68556-808-5

DEDICATION

This book is dedicated to all the dreamers who have had their wings clipped. May you find strength again in the name of Jesus.

TABLE OF CONTENTS

"It is not the critic who counts; not the man who points out how the strong man stumbles, or where the doer of deeds could have done them better. The credit belongs to the man who is actually in the arena, whose face is marred by dust and sweat and blood; who strives valiantly; who errs, who comes short again and again, because there is no effort without error and shortcoming; but who does actually strive to do the deeds; who knows great enthusiasms, the great devotions; who spends himself in a worthy cause; who at the best knows, in the end, the triumph of high achievement, and who at the worst, if he fails, at least fails while daring greatly, so that his place shall never be with those cold and timid souls who neither know victory nor defeat."

—Theodore Roosevelt

FOREWORD

I am writing this in one of the most polarizing times in our history as our world is experiencing a divide like no other time. Parties are fiercely divided in policy, racial tensions are at an all-time high, and the country is trying to navigate its way through a global pandemic. COVID-19 took everyone by surprise in the first quarter of 2020 as it ravaged China, Italy, and Europe before making its way to the states, sparking an almost immediate travel ban and the quarantining of sick individuals. What made it even more difficult is that we did not have a vaccine to combat this virus, forcing widespread panic, government regulations, and eventual state-mandated shutdowns of businesses, churches, schools, public beaches, and parks. This new normal forced people to adapt as many were reintroduced to their families either by furlough or stay-at-home orders. As if tensions were not already high, race relations took a nose-dive after the murder of George Floyd. In cities across America, riots broke out as people of all races came together in protest. It was the match that caused the wick of the American psyche to catch fire.

When people are forced to confine to a pattern of living that they are not accustomed to, there is always backlash. We found ourselves learning how to communicate through glass shields, face masks and having to navigate directional arrows at your local grocery store to "slow" the spread. The hope of tomorrow seemed distant as we vacillated between the ever-changing protocols that destroyed the free exchange of ideas and capitalism. Zoom meetings took off as businesses and people were forced to meet via screens to connect and get work done. Kids were also caught in the throngs as they were forced to go online for some time, stunting socialization and delaying critical developmental processes.

Will it ever be normal again? I'm not sure we are ever meant to get back to "normal." September 11, 2001, changed the way our nation looked at security protocols in our airports. We learned from it and made the necessary adjustments to help keep us safer. You didn't necessarily like the extra security measures, the pat-downs, and bag searches, but deep down, there was a sense of relief that our country was doing something to keep us safe.

Let's be honest, we don't often change unless it's absolutely necessary. A poor doctor's report, a death in the family, being fired from a job, or a failed relationship—all highlight the inevitability of life transitions. Much like a surprise global pandemic, these life-altering events can leave us embittered and cynical. These unexpected events have caused much of our world to be stuck. Like a marathon runner who physically can't take one more step, our society has remained stalled, but does it have to be this way? Unanswered questions lead people to draw their own conclusions resulting in unrest. Instead of order and peace, you have chaos and confusion. Although this may be a new season, this is not a new problem. Since the fall of man in Genesis 3, we have dealt with the repercussions of sin and lawlessness.

When people do not accept divine guidance, they run wild. But whoever obeys the law is joyful.
Proverbs 29:18 (NLT)

People who struggle with change will struggle with progress because it forces them to reconcile that they are not in control. Adam and Eve's sin caused a change in their utopian environment, but can you imagine if they would have halted life because they weren't living in paradise anymore? What about you? Has the last several years caused you to live bound? It could be fear of sickness or anger that things are not what they used to be. How can we truly play free when life feels so restrictive?

My prayer is that as you continue reading this book, you will see that since the fall, we have lived with some semblance of restrictions, but this has never and can never depict our freedom if we are in Christ. In any case, change is difficult, but it is only when we can learn to embrace it that we can begin to play free.

FOLLOW ME

Then he said to them all: "Whoever wants to be my disciple must deny themselves and take up their cross daily and follow me."

Luke 9:23 (NIV)

This command from Jesus has given us the blueprint to discover our real purpose in life. Contrary to the following craze of our social media platforms and popular news outlets, Jesus splits the narrative of social acceptance in two with a clear solution to being a follower. He didn't ask for us to follow a system, an idea, or a movement. Instead, He tells His disciples, "Follow me…" For many of His followers, this may have seemed like an invitation to literally follow Him around, learn from Him, listen to His words, and become a student of His teaching.

Although Jesus isn't physically present with us on the earth today, He still echoes through His word, "Follow me!" If you have read the Gospels, then you have undoubtedly been faced with some very unpopular feelings regarding Jesus' words. "Follow me" is nice, but when He starts to talk about eating His flesh and drinking His blood or hating family members, that becomes a step in the journey many are unwilling to take.

There has been a process that has existed from virtually the beginning of time involving public shunning. Early Greek history records a system of ostracism meant to banish an individual for causing a disruption in the flow of society or disrupting the cultural norms. I grew up in the '80s and '90s! Big hair, bomber jackets, Michael Jackson—this was life! Along with this culture, I also experienced its version of ostracism. We called it boycotting! As Christians, we boycotted anything and everything that represented secularism. Keep out the evil and only subscribe to Jesus. We waved our Jesus banners in church, shook our tambourines, and boycotted everything we were against.

Today, we are too "ordered" to banish someone, so instead, we cancel that person. Canceling someone or an organization is not a new practice; it may have changed names over the years, but it is certainly not new.

Christians living in today's society are suddenly on the receiving end of what it feels like to be canceled. If you don't believe me, invite your friend at work who is an atheist to church! You will quickly feel the shunning that so many have felt throughout history. Please hear me! I'm not making the claim that we shouldn't operate within boundaries. However, erecting invisible boundaries meant to "keep out evil" is a process Jesus neither participated in nor condoned. Jesus engaged the leaders of his day with unpopular truths that set them ablaze and ultimately caused them to hate Him. So, if we are going to follow Jesus, then it stands to reason that we may experience and should expect to be "canceled" by some, if not many.

Instead of speaking the truth in love, we have hidden behind a perverted version of love. Because we fear being canceled or unpopular, we skirt around the truth and never address sin, as the Word calls it. Inclusivity has crept its way in and masked itself as love. Here is where I believe we have stopped following Jesus and become ensnared or shackled to people. How can you truly play free if you are more concerned with how others will treat you in response to your obedience to Jesus? Here is the place I have to control my anger. Pastor friends reading this book, you have not been called to preach or teach your opinion on the Word of God. You have been called by our Savior to speak the truth in love. You don't get a pass on this. You are sacrificing the freedom of your congregation and crippling their growth as believers. We have to stand on the truth found only in the Word. Stop winking at sin by looking the other way. If you know your worship leader is struggling with sin, do what is right. The fear that your worship set on Sunday may take a hit only teaches and reinforces your sin sickness. Follow Jesus and play free!

THE SETUP

Do you know why you were created? You are not just some abstract thought that one day appeared in human form and now somehow must try and navigate the various seasons and complexities of life alone. You are the depiction of an artist, a Picasso, the revelation of someone's thought, the creation of what He had in mind. David writes in the book of Psalms:

You made all the delicate, inner parts of my body and knit me together in my mother's womb. Thank you for making me so wonderfully complex! Your workmanship is marvelous— how well I know it.

Psalm 139:13–14 (NLT)

You are the focal point of what the Creator envisioned. With all your complexity and symmetry, you showcase His wonderful handiwork. There is none like you, nor will there ever be one like you. You are one of a kind. You are the prized portrait bought at an auction, sold to the highest bidder. He has picked you out of a crowd and chosen to tell His story of redemption. Redemption—the action of saving or being saved from sin, error, or evil. Isn't that mankind's greatest need? The ability to be rescued from ourselves. To be brought back into right standing with the One we have sinned against by falling short of His perfect standard. The world hasn't been right since sin made its introduction onto the world's stage in Genesis 3. Grappling with its effects, we wage wars trying to curb its appetite. We lust because of it. We nip, tuck, lengthen, and shrink because of it, desperately trying to fix the path of destruction it has left inside each one of us. We try to hide in the cracks of life in order to avoid its reality… However, looking into a mirror tells the truth about its effects. We are outwardly perishing. To the nonbeliever, it can be traumatic. To the believer, it is essential…

> *Therefore we do not lose heart. Though outwardly we are wasting away, yet inwardly we are being renewed day by day. For our light and momentary troubles are achieving for us an eternal glory that far outweighs them all.*
>
> **2 Corinthians 4:16–17 (NIV)**

The endgame is glory. We are destined to spend eternity with the One who created us. There's nothing wrong with feeling good about yourself, but it crosses over into dysfunction when we look for unhealthy validation from others, prioritizing their opinion over our own. Live your life, take care of the body that God has given you but know where your true worth lies. Your "defects" are what make you human. God has designed you with a specific purpose in mind and cut you to fit in this time in history. With all your crazy and outbursts of irrationality, God still has something in store for you. To try and cover up the real you would be a travesty robbing the world of the gift God created you to be. Jesus' invitation to follow Him is a journey into self-discovery. To a place of wonder. To get to know the Author of life and His original purpose for life. To get some answers to some of life's greatest questions we ask today…Why am I here? Where do I fit? The answers to these questions will lead you into some of your greatest discoveries about who you are, but they will also lead you down some dangerous paths that will bring you face to face with some of your greatest enemies. This is not for the faint of heart. There is a cost to following Jesus. There are no magic pills or quick fixes. I'm hard-pressed to tell you the truth so you don't get pulled into a misguided view of Christianity. Like a prized fighter defending his belt, there will be challenges that threaten to take you out. Side effects may include nausea, vomiting, anxiety, feelings of abandonment, and isolation. These may not be the full list of side effects. For a full list of possible side effects, please consult your physician. I want to apologize on behalf of Christian leaders if you were never told that you would have to fight in this fight. That going to church is not enough. That listening to cute sermons on Sunday is not enough. We have fallen into the trap of consumerism in the church today, relying on the pastor or leaders to spoon-feed us our weekly dose of spirituality. This has bred weak, ineffective Christians ınot hold their own when they are thrust into the ıd forced to fight. Yes, I'll say it again. You are t! You are going to have to roll up your sleeves and learn to feed yourself. Find out what God's word says about you, your life, and your place in His story. Follow the clues that have been embedded in your makeup. Why? Because there is an enemy who prowls around like a roaring lion, looking for someone to devour (see 1 Peter 5:8). He knows your tendencies and where you are weak. He will hit you below the belt to test your commitment and resolve. You will have to fight your way through some messy terrain, ravenous storms and leave your past behind if you're going to crossover into all that God has for you. But how bad do you want to be free? Bad enough to get dirty? To actually play to win?

This game is not fair, but it is a good fight of faith. Our Commander and Chief, Jesus, is in our corner. He has already won the ultimate victory with His death on the cross. He is alive and well, ever living to make intercession for us (see Hebrews 7:25). Can't you see it? Looking back over your life, aren't you the least bit curious as to how you got here? Can't you see the providential hand of destiny at work? Even in the darkest times, there has been Someone who has guided your life. Isn't there a bit of curiosity that drives you to find the answers as to why you are the way you are? Isn't the fact that you have made it through some strange seasons a testament to divine guidance at work in your life? I realize that this may be difficult to swallow, given the current state of our world and the history that preceded it. But there is Someone who has been writing the story. It's History (His story). You are not an accident. You were born in your generation for a reason. You were placed in your family for a reason. You grew up on your side of town for a reason. Trained by the environment that helped nurture you, you blossomed into the person you are today. At a young age, you learned to suckle from life's disappointments. You were your first secretary, taking notes and learning to translate the signals that life and your environment were sending. You learned to file life's events under different categories: Pleasure. Shame. Rejection. Abuse. Mistreated. Not good enough. These became the leading headlines of your life. They were etched in the chasm of your mind and began to affect how you related to the world around you. You attempted to fill in the gaps with solutions that were quick and satisfying, only to find out that those solutions were temporary and unfulfilling. Not knowing where to turn, you were introduced to doors that so many are still struggling to close today: pornography, lust, sexual misconduct. Fill in the blank. These doors became the mirrors that you looked into when you needed a fix. They barricaded you behind the real issues that were festering beneath the surface. Addicted at a young age, you approached your teenage years and young adulthood broken and damaged. It was there you met social stigmas and her friend peer pressure. Together they forced you into a lifestyle you thought you were ready for but weren't. Freedom from rules and accountability became attractive to you, but you really weren't ready for the responsibility that came with freedom. When you look back now, you can see that you grew up crooked. You grew up too early. Your parents lacked the necessary skills in order to raise you right, and as a result, roots of rejection and bitterness have embedded themselves inside of you that still have not come up fully yet. Many are still playing with pacifiers in their mouth when it comes to life. They can't self-regulate or chew on truth. Conforming is not delivering on its promise to give you the peace that you are looking for. Pleasure is lying to you. You know there is a desire for something deeper. You tried to fill it with people and possessions, but it doesn't work. Why? It's because you were created with a God-shaped hole that only He can fill. If you're honest, it's always been there. Deep down, when no one is looking, you question the validity of what you heard growing up. Get a job. Find a mate. Have some kids. Be normal. That will fix it. That will help alleviate the sinking feeling of not being whole. While those things are blessings, they are rudimentary in the pursuit of fulfillment and acceptance. I want you to think about all that you have done in order to be accepted. Has it really paid off for you? Are you living a robust life? Have you lost yourself in the process? Are you bleeding out? Until those holes are filled with the right thing, there will always be a deficit when it comes to your fulfillment. The good news is, is that they can. That's why Jesus came!

Jesus answered, *"I am the way and the truth and the life. No one comes to the Father except through me."*

John 14:6 (NIV)

He is the way (3598—*hodos*).

Usage: a way, a road, a journey, a path. (Bible Hub, n.d.)

If you want to find the way, you must follow Jesus, not a religion. You must be willing to forgo what you think you know for what you don't. This is where the struggle for most people is, as many have predetermined what a relationship with Jesus Christ looks like based on what they have experienced themselves in a church or seen from those who have called themselves Christians. Based on those experiences, they have a view of Jesus that may not be correct. Do you blame them? Hypocrisy has crippled the validity of what a real walk with Jesus Christ looks like. Lifestyle choices of those who call themselves Christians have brought into view the stark reality of many who are playing church. Living with your boyfriend or girlfriend and showing up to church on Sunday with hands raised in worship is not a billboard for successful Christianity. Quit playing! You are turning off others to the exclusivity of the gospel. It requires a dying to self. We have painted a picture of a Jesus who is all-forgiving and all-loving and whose grace covers everything. We have demasculinized Him making Him out to be some love-sick heartthrob who gave His life so that we can live any way we want to. Nor is He the Jesus with the forlorn face and sad eyes that you see in pictures. He is not asking for your pity! He doesn't need it. He wants your obedience. Religious ceremonies are infatuated with the inauspicious way that He died, forgetting that He rose from the dead! They fawn over His death but fail to celebrate His resurrection! I am all for remembering His sacrifice, but let's not forget that He ever lives to make intercession for us (see Hebrews 7:25). In an effort to be inclusive, we have left the guardrails of the Bible that bring us into His intended purpose for our life, life! Hear what I'm saying. I'm not talking about being perfect. No one is. But I am talking about being perfected. There should be some evidence that salvation is working in your life. Stop confessing Jesus as Lord when you don't really follow. Others are making decisions based on what they see you do. I know you may not want that type of influence, but the reality is that people will follow what you follow, especially if they see it working in your life. Perhaps there is a disconnect between what people say and what people do because they don't understand what He did for us by closing the gap that separated us from Him by His death on the cross. Sin separated us from Him. His blood was the price that atoned for that sin. Jesus is and will always be the Way, the Truth, and the Life (see John 14:6).

The fact that He takes the time to articulate this to His disciples makes it even more impactful. He is not looking for robots. He is looking for people who are willing to go the distance with Him and follow Him with their whole hearts. He is after inward transformation, not an outward display of works that amount to nothing. He wants you well. Have you become so politically correct that you have lost your way? Compromised on truth? Take up Jesus' invitation to follow Him.

TRENDING

For we are not fighting against flesh-and-blood enemies, but against evil rulers and authorities of the unseen world, against mighty powers in this dark world, and against evil spirits in the heavenly places.

Ephesians 6:12 (NLT)

As a Christian, I am concerned for the state of the church. According to Gallup, US church membership has fallen below 50 percent for the first time.

Americans' membership in houses of worship continued to decline last year, dropping below 50% for the first time in Gallup's eight-decade trend. In 2020, 47% of Americans said they belonged to a church, synagogue or mosque, down from 50% in 2018 and 70% in 1999.

Jeffrey M Jones
Politics, March 29, 2021

The reality of the pandemic has rocked the world and the church. It has given way to a *woke* culture that has infiltrated our churches, homes, and the way we do business. Intellectual skepticism dominates news headlines and conversations, and we are forced to listen to people who want to rethink and reshape our past, our ideals, and our culture. However, I would propose that looking back at our past too long can be detrimental. We can learn from it, but we can't remake it. While it is beneficial to revisit past victories and defeats, it can also capsize your momentum and rob you of the satisfaction of how far you have come. By "staying back," we are missing our future, robbing ourselves of the creativity and the possibility of tomorrow. I am all for rethinking how we do things, but erasing history is a slap in the face to God and to the men and women that fought and died to get us here today. It is an attack on the grace that was once sufficient for that period in history. Trying to reframe history so that it is more digestible doesn't negate its reality. Sacrifices were made. Blood was shed. Lives were given for your freedom. That's the reality. Tearing down statues doesn't alleviate the impact those men had on our nation. This pandemic has revealed the cracks in our morality and spirituality. Isolation is not the answer. It retards essential developmental processes and gives people a license to hide. What should have been a temporary hibernation period has turned into an extended stay. A new wave of online churchgoers has emerged because of it and has made it comfortable for people to stay at home, taking them away from the rich community that God designed them to be in. We were meant to be social. Left to ourselves and devoid of human interaction, we run the risk of slipping into self-loathing and deprivation.

We are at a tipping point as a nation. Recent events have given rise to cancel culture. Cancel culture is defined as the practice or tendency of engaging in mass canceling as a way of expressing disapproval and exerting social pressure. (Merriam-Webster, n.d.)

In other words, If I don't agree with you or subscribe to your point of view, then I am at risk of being shunned. If I don't run in the same circles, hold to the same belief system as a group, or conform to the popular thinking of the day, then I run the risk of being publicly shamed, ridiculed, or even threatened. We are living in a fantasy world when we try to create a utopian society where everyone gets along, believes the same, and drives the same energy-efficient cars. Diversity is what makes the world a beautiful place. Creativity showcases the beauty and intricacy of God as we paint on the canvas of life with the different brushes that God has created each one of us to use. Society would become stagnant and stale if we conformed to an ideological oneness where there was no ability to debate ideas and confront systems that are not working. That is called *communism*. The ability to find faster routes, a better process, and a more individualized sense of destiny is what makes us great. It's what makes our founding so liberating. We wanted freedom, and we fought to get it. Those sacrifices of men and women who have gone before us have afforded us the ability to live freely. Freedom is your God-given right. You were created to be free. Jesus died so you can be free. Anything that tries to hinder that freedom is in direct opposition to why you were created. We are missing the mark. Shifting values and viewpoints are counter punching at our attempts to walk in divine destiny. We are in a battle to conform. To lose the sense of individualism and identity we were created with. We have gotten to this point over time as lack of a moral compass and deviation from the *truth* have set us adrift, sailing the seas of compromise. In short, we have become prisoners in our own land, forgetting the ideals that this country was founded on. We are fighting one another, blind to the reality that we are not fighting in a seen war but are wrestling against evil rulers and authorities of the unseen world, against mighty powers in this dark world, and against evil spirits in the heavenly places (see Ephesians 6:12).

We are fighting against forces that we cannot see. The same forces that tempted Adam and Eve in the garden are the same forces we are fighting today. These forces influence decisions and the ebb and flow of society. Once a year, we are reminded around Halloween about these forces as movies are made depicting the Hollywood version of the demonic. Producers do the best they can to try and scare you into believing that there is something "out there." There is! You are being watched. Your affections, attitudes, and appetites are constantly under surveillance. The enemy is taking notes and waiting for the opportunity to break into your life. His access point? Unresolved issues from your childhood. He will pepper those wounds from your past to soften your outlook on what is truth and what is a lie.

I understand the reality of what might be happening in your life right now. I also understand that there is a God who sees it all. Have you stopped and asked yourself, "What am I supposed to learn from this season?" No matter how difficult it has been, it has presented itself with various opportunities for self-introspection.

Here's what I do know…

God does not abdicate responsibility because the world is out of control. He does not shift His gaze or change His mind based upon the changing seasons or the changing minds of the people He created. He holds the seasons in His hands. He is going to do what He has already planned to do! This is a wake-up call to the world to look toward heaven for answers. Jesus is coming quickly! While you are stuck fighting yourself, there is an unseen enemy who is out to destroy you. He would like nothing more for you to cave and give up. Wake up!

God is waiting on us to move through our issues so we can become who He has called us to be. The Spirit of God is constantly urging (and sometimes irritating) us to let go of past hurts and regrets and step into the life that God has promised, the life that Jesus died to give you. He knows what's waiting on the other side of your pain. Don't be a victim. Too many are captive to their past and blame others for the way their life has turned out. Stop blaming others! It is unhealthy and unproductive for you to stay stuck in a cycle of blame-shifting that leads to incapacitated growth. Why can't you move on? Why can't you get another job? Why can't you find another relationship? Do you honestly think that your future is decided by your past? It might have played a role in how you got to where you are today, but it doesn't dictate how your story will end.

We have been given an opportunity to live. To move forward and take possession of the promises of God. To move past the lingering effects of our past and into a brighter future. The question is, do you want to? Do you have the guts to see past where you are? Do you believe that there is more to life than what you have experienced? If so, it might mean you have to change the way you think about yourself and look at your life. It can get messy, but how bad do you want to be free?

Fainting Goats

The medical dictionary defines a "fainting goat" as a breed of domestic goats which carries the gene for myotonia congenita which causes its muscles to stiffen for 5–10 seconds when startled, which often causes them to fall over ('faint'); they are otherwise completely normal.

When we continue in life, we undoubtedly are going to face opposition. When you think about the birthing process, it was a miracle that you made it out. Passing through the birth canal was a traumatic experience for both you and your mother. I still have the forceps marks on my head to prove it. As a baby, you are faced with the reality of moving from a protective state inside your mother into an exposed state. Leaving the umbilical cord behind, you are introduced to a bottle or a breast where you learn what it means to be fed. You also learned how to respond to life. Either by crying or soiling your diaper, you put those around you on alert that you need attention. It was a sign that something was wrong. That something must change. Fast forward to your life today. How you respond to life says a lot about you, and it is an indicator of your level of resilience. What you believe about yourself is tested most when you are under pressure. I want you to notice something about these goats. Upon further study, you'll find that the goats remain conscious even after they faint. They are aware of what's happening but paralyzed by fear. I wonder how many of us are like these goats. When encountering resistance or pressure, we seize up and go catatonic. Conscious but unresponsive. Our flight response kicks in, and we play dead. Unable to respond and deal with the stress of life, we look for ways to cope that are unhealthy, further thrusting us into a downward spiral of immobility. Can you relate?

From a biblical standpoint, we have been given spiritual weapons to fight in this spiritual battle.

We use God's mighty weapons, not worldly weapons, to knock down the strongholds of human reasoning and to destroy false arguments.

2 Corinthians 10:4 (NLT)

A *stronghold*, according to a HELPS word study, is used figuratively as a *false argument* in which a person seeks "shelter" ("a safe place") to *escape reality*.

What reality are you trying to escape? What do you

escape to in order to quell the worry and anxiety? What emotional crutches do you lean on to pacify the aching impulses that shoot through your soul daily? On the contrary, who do you know in your life that always seems to be pushing forward and winning? It's not that they don't have problems, but they have learned to face them in Christ's strength. I am convinced that it is the way that you look at your life that makes the difference. Pressure is a privilege. It affords you the opportunity to hone in on your ability to respond. It measures your resiliency and gives you a platform to either rise above the challenges you are facing or succumb to them. You can't expect to go through life unscathed by issues. Life is a wide net of entanglements that you will have to sort through if you want to win. Insulating yourself from the ferocity of life weakens your response system. Exposure is inevitable. It is a ploy of the enemy to get you isolated. If he can weaken your cognitive ability to stand on truth, your chance of winning diminishes. I am writing this book to sound the alarm. Wake up! You are in a fight! Your mind is the battlefield. You are being targeted by an enemy who knows the frailty of human reasoning. What are you listening to right now? Who are you listening to right now? You are weak. The enemy knows you are weak. He will do everything he can to prey on that weakness. Fear is his greatest weapon. If he can get you to turn inward, he can bury you with self-doubt and trepidation. Don't let him do it. Turn outward. Live your life in spite of the fear. As a side note, I realize that most of you might be required to wear a mask if you are in a business that requires it. However, take your mask off in the car! No one is around you? Breathe. You are letting the fear of what if dictate what may never be. You need to break out of the cocoon of fear that so many are in. Breaking out of the cycle, however, will require strategy. This is not a normal fight. It is spiritual and thus requires a spiritual strategy. You will have to tap into the supernatural if you are going to win.

Feel Not

Your mindset is deeply rooted in your emotional well-being. If you can fix the emotional gaps and cracks in your life, the way you see yourself in the face of the opposition will change. Our perspective about ourselves changes as we begin to come into agreement with our worth and value. If you know you are loved, it changes what you will allow dictating how you live. What have you given permission to control you? What psycho-social components have crept into your thought process that doesn't need to be there? You deserve to be happy. Who told you that you couldn't be? You deserve to be free. Who told you that you couldn't be? Have you let someone define your borders of happiness? Have you left it up to someone else to tell you what you can and cannot be? Have you let their small-minded thinking cap you? Has your need to be needed crippled your sense of individuality and self-worth? Until that is unraveled, you will remain tied into the idea that someone else's happiness is more important than your own. You are worthy to receive all that God has promised to you. But you have to see it first. You have a right to life because of the One who died to give it to you. But you have to want it. If you can accept your past, the way you are wired, and the leading of the Holy Spirit, you can begin to carve out the right paths in life that best fit your DNA. I am convinced that many people are playing in fields that they don't have the grace for. Are you running with individuals who don't hold the same core values as they do? You will not get very far as sooner or later there will be a power struggle. The result: power outages. Why? Because compromise gives way to a weakened immune system and leaves you susceptible to sickness. Not necessarily physical sickness, but emotional sickness. Dysfunction is a game that has no parameters. Erratic emotions can handcuff you to undeserving partners and keep you bound in self-loathing and defeatism. If you can rebuild your emotional well-being, you will have an easier time steering away from the cliffs that you were never meant to jump off, resulting in your emotional health. Isn't that what you ultimately are looking for? Or should be looking for?

If you let yourself get caught up in distractions, you will miss the opportunities to learn vital life lessons that will help lead you on your path to success. You might be asking yourself, what does it matter anyway? The world is burning. Things are out of control. Where is God? God has not hidden Himself to the point where He cannot be found. He has not abdicated His throne just because things are out of *your* control. It just might require that you look a little deeper for Him. Do you know where to find Him? Move away from the shores of convenience out into the deep where faith is required. God is lurking there. But you must be willing to leave the temporary satisfaction of comfort and pleasure for the rocky seas of confrontation and the unknown. It is there that you will discover the true riches of life and godliness. Will there be obstacles? Yes. Your biggest obstacle to these discoveries will be you. Self-preservation is the enemy of discovery. Until you let go of the possible outcomes, you will remain stuck, and you will miss out on the joy of losing your life to gain it. Your security is an enemy to your freedom. It is an outlier with no real, lasting results and robs you of your purpose. Are you willing to get to the end of your life and wonder what could have been? To miss out on the best because you valued security over purpose? There is no security apart from God! There are no guarantees! You can't find what you're looking for in a person, place, or thing. It is only found in God. *C'mon!* Haven't you discovered this yet? People are fickle, and life is too complicated for you to put your trust in them.

Author Don Marquis said, "Ours is a world where people don't know what they want and are willing to go through hell to get it."

It's true. You can't expect to follow someone who needs to be led themselves. We cannot continue to expect the same if we are going to see a move of God in our lifetime. He is moving. The stage is being set for His return. Hell is nervous. The enemy is showing his hand. There is an assault on Christian values and identity. Gender confusion has hit the streets, our movie screens, and even our churches. Our kids are being introduced to pictures portraying Bob and Jim as a couple who love each other. They are being encouraged to question their own sexuality and explore who they really are. Promiscuity is rampant, even in mainstream churches. People are looking for love in unusual places. "Feeling" not right about who they are, they are mutilating themselves to find answers. Here is the problem. The way I feel about something doesn't make the truth obsolete. This is my issue with cancel culture. Just because you don't like something or someone doesn't mean their impact never happened. Erasing them or tearing down statues doesn't make their life irrelevant. Freedom rings. It echoes throughout history, whether you like it or not. No amount of rhetoric, misguided solutions, or pandering will stop its power. Something *must* shift in our mentality. My wife and I run an online fitness business called C3 Athletics. One of the joys of being in a fitness community is being able to see people push past limitations and break past barriers that have been set up in their minds, either by choice or force. We have discovered that there is a definite correlation between breaking past physical barriers and mental barriers. If I can train my mind to push past pain and temporary discomfort, I can begin to take back control of my life. My feelings don't dictate who I am. They are a part of me, but they don't define me. Mind trumps matter. Can trumps can't. This mindset bleeds over into other areas of life as well, leading to emotional, spiritual, and even financial health. The trajectory of your life begins to change as you see past the trauma of the past into the possibility of tomorrow. There *is* a tomorrow! Life doesn't stop just because you were blindsided or because there is a pandemic.

It may be altered, but it keeps moving. Even in the midst of turmoil and confusion, you can still make strides to become a better you. Climate change is a must. We must shift from basking in the scorching heat of yesterday's battles to the cool breeze of a promise for tomorrow. Yesterday is dead. Today is what we have been given. There is hope for tomorrow. But it will not come without sacrifice and pain. There will be other battles to face, and you will need the strength and resources to fight them. Playing free means letting go of your past and how you thought your life should be. I know many of you are battle-weary. But you have made it this far. Why not jump into the unknown and allow God to strengthen you? Your best days are ahead. Fight!

FIGHT!

For God has not given us a spirit of fear and timidity, but of power, love, and self-discipline.

2 Timothy 1:7 (NLT)

Toilet bowling is a phrase that my mother-in-law uses when referring to the downward cycle our thoughts can lead us to if unchecked. I experienced the effects of toilet bowling firsthand on a mission trip I had the privilege of leading some years ago to Ecuador. It was a small team tasked with the assignment of reaching the Shuar people in the Amazon of Ecuador. It was a life-changing trip. The trip was well worth the sacrifice to get there, as we were able to continue to help the boots on the ground continue to make inroads with this indigenous tribe.

Did I say sacrifice? Let's rewind to the flight into Quito, Ecuador. My eyes were in amazement as we got onto the tarmac to get ready to board the plane. I was a little nervous as the plane was smaller than I was used to. To give you a little perspective, I was in the back of the plane, and the seats behind me were used for extra luggage! Already a little hesitant, I buckled my seatbelt and grabbed the armrests next to me as we got ready to take off. Thankfully, I knew the woman next to me. She was a member of our team and felt some comfort in knowing that I had someone who could pray if things went bad. As we got ready to take off, I felt the anxiety kick in. After only several minutes of being in the air, the plane hit an air pocket and dropped suddenly, veering to the right. Panic set in. I gripped the armrest bracing for another drop. Sure enough, it happened again. The fight was on. It was either fight or flight.

According to verywellmind.com, *the fight-or-flight response (also known as the acute stress response) refers to a physiological reaction that occurs when we are in the presence of something that is mentally or physically terrifying. The fight-or-flight response is triggered by the release of hormones that prepare your body to either stay and deal with a threat or to run away to safety.*

Where was I going to go? I had to just take it and hope that we made it. This went on for the duration of the 45-minute flight into Ecuador. Periods of reprieve were short, and it was impossible to rest. What amazed me was that there were actually people sleeping on this flight! I did what I thought was best. I retreated into that place of uncertainty, tried to think happy thoughts, and braced my core. The only problem was that my breathing was erratic, and I ended up passing out on the woman next to me. LOL! It was not until later that I realized that most of our team had gotten sick and puked. What made matters worse was that the pilot did not say anything to us for the duration of the flight! All he did was smile at us as we got off the airplane. After a few hours of rest, I was good to go, and we had a great trip. Some of you might be thinking, *What about the airplane ride back from Ecuador?* It was perfect. Such is life.

There were some valuable lessons that I learned from this flight.

When storms come, we have a choice on how we respond. I was not as strong as I thought. Mentally I was weak. My coping mechanism jammed my ability to withstand the uncertainty of the turbulence. It was an indicator that the check engine light was on and that something had to change in me

Storms also expose our true power source. They test what we are connected to. Facing them gives us an edge as we know *Who* is with us through it. The problem is when we forget the power that lies within us to confront the storm. Instead of taking it on, we run from it, thinking that somehow running from it is going to make it go away. Or worse, we end up doing nothing and allow the storm to cripple us with its ferocity, forcing us further into a paralytic state. Face them now or face them later. Either way, they will catch up with you in another season. As I have found over the years, God has a long memory. He always remembers where we are on our journey and what lessons need to be learned.

Cheer Dad

I have had the privilege of being at some of my daughter's cheerleading practices over the past year. You would think that these girls just get together and do some routines and call it a night. Not so. There are several age groups represented from ages six through middle school. While the girls are practicing, there are football teams practicing at the same time. It is a fabulous combination of cheer and grit as teams of all ages are working, learning, and perfecting routines. One particular situation caught my attention. A group of boys was practicing on a field adjacent to where my daughter's team was practicing. Keep in mind that these boys have barely begun to break four feet and are learning the basics of what it means to play football. The coaches have them mimicking a football drill where each player lines up against one another. The object of the drill is for the player with the ball to get past the defender. Easy enough, right? Except they put the boys inside cones, so they are forced to face one another. As the person with the ball approaches, the defender is "supposed" to tackle them. Lol. However, with these boys, the fear of being hit or tackling becomes very evident as the ball carrier comes at them. Some are "playing" and doing everything they can to minimize contact. The coaches are imploring the kids to stay in it and finish. They know what the kids don't know. If the kids don't get used to contact and get over the fear of being hit, they are never going to make it in the game! One particular kid got my attention. He was struggling. The coaches knew he was struggling. Yet, they did not let him get out of the drill without making him confront his fears. With tears streaming down his face, they made him continue to do the drill until he got used to the contact. What made this a glorious event to watch was the fact that his mother was on the other side of the fence, watching her son struggle. She was constantly throwing out words of encouragement to her son as he would get back in line to "try again." She would shout, "I want to see you fight." "Show me that you can fight." It fired me up! This process went on for a few minutes with him as she implored him to get up and do better. What amazed me was the ferocity of the mother as she tried to get her son to reach deep and tap into what was already there, yet not realized. She was trying to help him break out of the fear of what was stopping him and break into what was possible. And he did! He finally made contact and stayed in it long enough until the drill was over. What a picture! I got a glimpse into the way God looks at us. Like a parent standing outside the fence of life, He implores us to fight for what He has given us: the opportunities, the gifts, and the relationships. To rid ourselves of limited mindsets that stunt our potential and hinder us from reaching our goals. To take the hits and keep getting back up. Knowing that every time we do, it lessens the grip that fear has on us and causes us to break out of the shell of infertility and into the realm of possibility. We have been given a marvelous opportunity to become all that God has designed for us, but sadly there are many who are "playing" at life. Refusing to hit or be hit, they never throw themselves fully at something long enough to experience a breakthrough because they fear what the impact might look like. They are too afraid of failure and, in some cases, success. Hello! Doesn't everything involve a risk? Risk and reward are all part of the circle of life. The reality is that if you can't face opposition, it is going to be very difficult to be successful in life and grow strong enough to hold the weight of success as you break into new territories. If you cannot step out of your comfort zone, you will never break into the fullness of what God has for you.

Time for Change

Every single day we have a lane to run in. In the lane next to you, there are principalities, powers, and the rulers of the darkness of this age (see Ephesians 6:12). They are making their advancement toward you, trying to trip you up so that you don't cross the finish line. They will do everything they can to get you to run out of your lane and sabotage your progress by reminding you of your past failures. When you agree with their assessment, you fall back in the race, failing to keep pace with the One who is running with you. Therefore, it is important to know *whose* you are so you can face each day with confidence. If you are struggling with confidence, it is time to start creating an environment of positive reinforcement. See yourself winning. I know it can be difficult, but you must change the narrative of your story. If you quit every time you face something difficult, you further prove to your enemies that you don't have what it takes. Flip the script. Change your story by allowing God to rewrite some of the manuscripts of your life. Could it be that God wants to show you some things about yourself and about who He is? To break you out of the blanket of fear and insecurity that you have wrapped yourself in? To finally get you to see yourself how He sees you? Perception plays a huge part in how you see yourself and the world. It is the key to your position in life and what opportunities you feel like you have. You can stay in the shade for fear of being burned, but you will miss out on the richest blessing of being seasoned by life. Seasons come and go. The writer in Ecclesiastes 3 reminds us of changing seasons:

> *There is a time for everything, and a season for every activity under the heavens: a time to be born and a time to die, a time to plant and a time to uproot, a time to kill and a time to heal, a time to tear down and a time to build, a time to weep and a time to laugh, a time to mourn and a time to dance, a time to scatter stones and a time to gather them, a time to embrace and a time to refrain from embracing, a time to search and a time to give up, a time to keep and a time to throw away, a time to tear and a time to mend, a time to be silent and a time to speak, a time to love and a time to hate, a time for war and a time for peace.*
>
> **Ecclesiastes 3:1–8 (NIV)**

Growing up, you learned valuable lessons about life, love, and acceptance. You also learned about loss and disappointment. Whether you realize it or not, how you handled disappointment shaped how you process it today. Furthermore, how you handle disappointment determines the level of progress you will make in your life. If you can see beyond your temporary disillusionment, you will see that setbacks are often gifts in disguise and the grounds from which great things are forged. This life is a beautiful mess of constructs that are erected during some of the most challenging seasons of life. Vanilla is not the only flavor of ice cream. Yet, so many live vanilla lives, following the same rituals and routines that their parents followed, never exploring other sides of life. What side of life are you living in right now? Have you barricaded yourself beneath the bars of safety, thinking that comfort is your best protection against being hurt? Have you closed shop, locking the doors to your heart to keep anything good from getting in? I am not saying that wisdom is not needed when it comes to what you will allow and what you don't allow to partner with you in life. Boundaries are essential. But are you really living if you're not risking? In your attempt to save your life, you are really losing it. We have what I call a Low T problem in the body of Christ today. Not the Low T problem you're thinking about (see Roman for that, *wink*). A *Low Try* problem. People have settled for mediocrity and second best instead of excellence and first. Rather than put in the work to get better, they have drifted into laziness and compromise, and as a result, they have grey-blended the Bible to suit lifestyles that are neither powerful nor effective. We can't afford to continue in the same cycles of spiritual malnutrition and co-dependency that plague the lives of so many in our culture. Our churches are filled with pastors who are entertainment-driven. The power of the gospel has been reduced to a wick that is barely lit, leaving Christians impotent in the face of opposition. We have done a disservice to people by teaching them to rely on self-help manuals and the pastor rather than on the power of the Holy Spirit. They lack the fundamentals of the faith and cannot "feed" themselves spiritually. They have been spoon-fed a gospel that is barely relevant and, as a result, are impotent when it comes to resisting the enemy. Passive Christianity does not work. It has never worked! You are going to have to get into the Word of God yourself and find out what God's heart is for you. It is *not* just to sit on a pew or chair on Sunday morning once a week to listen to someone tell you how to live your best life. While it is essential to gather together in order to spur one another on to good works (see Hebrews 10:24), you are going to have to start feeding yourself and building strength on your own if you are going to make it in today's world. If you can see yourself as God sees you, then you'll begin to step out in faith and take a shot at the dreams that are bubbling up inside you. If you see yourself as inferior, you will sit on your potential and die a slow death of hopelessness. You must fight for yourself! No one can do it for you. Where do you begin? It starts with an honest self-assessment of where you are. Self-efficacy is a vital component of that assessment.

Self-efficacy refers to an individual's belief in his or her capacity to execute behaviors necessary to produce specific performance attainments. (Bandura, 1977, 1986, 1997)

Low self-efficacy opens the door to underachievement and widens the gap between your reality and what's possible. Progress is possible. Achievement is possible. Victory is possible. But it does not come without lacing up your shoes and playing in the game.

Throw What You Know

I defy the armies of Israel today! Send me a man who will fight me! When Saul and the Israelites heard this, they were terrified and deeply shaken.

1 Samuel 17:10–11 (NLT)

The Israelites once again find themselves fighting a battle against the Philistines. They are in the Valley of Elah with the Israelites on one hill and the Philistines on the other when the giant Goliath offers a solution. Sadly, the response is all too common when trouble comes calling: *dismayed and terrified.* No fight, just "flighting" in place. This took place for 40 days:

For forty days, every morning and evening, the Philistine champion strutted in front of the Israelite army.

1 Samuel 17:16 (NLT)

What about you? What is shouting out to you every morning when you wake up? What is calling you into battle? Is it a fear that keeps ripping through you like a sharp object causing you to bleed out emotionally? Is it a past regret that keeps choking your progress and blocking your ability to receive God's love and forgiveness?

David asked the soldiers standing nearby, "What will a man get for killing this Philistine and ending his defiance of Israel? Who is this pagan Philistine anyway, that he is allowed to defy the armies of the living God?"

1 Samuel 17:26 (NLT)

After a discussion on what would be given to the man who defeats Goliath, David has a conversation with Saul:

"Don't worry about this Philistine," David told Saul. "I'll go fight him!" "Don't be ridiculous!" Saul replied. "There's no way you can fight this Philistine and possibly win! You're only a boy, and he's been a man of war since his youth."

1 Samuel 17:32–33 (NLT)

Check out David's response in verses 36–37:

I have done this to both lions and bears, and I'll do it to this pagan Philistine, too, for he has defied the armies of the living God! The Lord who rescued me from the claws of the lion and the bear will rescue me from this Philistine!" Saul finally consented. "All right, go ahead," he said. "And may the Lord be with you!"

David knew who he was, and he knew who God was. He had seen God deliver him from enemies before. Do you know who you are? The answer to that question will determine if and how quickly you confront what is confronting you.

> *As Goliath moved closer to attack, David quickly ran out to meet him. Reaching into his shepherd's bag and taking out a stone, he hurled it with his sling and hit the Philistine in the forehead. The stone sank in, and Goliath stumbled and fell face down on the ground.*
>
> **1 Samuel 17:48–49 (NLT)**

I want to point out a key element in this verse. David runs to meet Goliath as he advances; he doesn't run the other way or decide that he's too big.

What is it going to take for you to stand up to your giant? Passive engagement and wishing it away will not make it go away. You have to be willing to face it if you are going to beat it. Go after it! Think about the times in your life that you beat something that was threatening to take you out. Cancer? Obesity? Relationship dysfunction? Your own attitude? Remember what it took to get you there. Remember that the same God who helped you through that will be the same God that will help you deal with what is threatening you today. Throw what you know at it! Leverage yesterday's victories against today's opponent. Look at your scars. They serve as a reminder of how far you've come! Turn and face it. It might be different and more daunting than the last one, but giants come in all shapes and sizes. Just because you won yesterday doesn't mean there is not another opponent ready to call you out today. They keep coming! Take sports as an example.

When a team finishes dealing with one opponent, they usually watch the film to evaluate the game, dissect what they did wrong, and start game-planning for the next opponent. The next opponent is doing the same thing as they get ready to face them. They want to beat you.

They dissect your weakness and evaluate matchups they think will swing in their favor. You don't get a reward for just showing up, and teams don't feel sorry for you. As Herman Edwards, former Head Coach of the New York Jets, said, "You play to win the game." No one wants to lose. Your enemy is the same way. He wants to win. You might have beaten a giant in one season of your life, but he will come back in another form to try and defeat you on another front. This might seem superfluous, seeing that the enemy has already been defeated. But if he is one thing, he is persistent. He is a pest that needs to be swatted time and time again. Stay in the game. Sharpen your skills. The blessing is getting to fight against him, knowing that he *has* already been defeated because the One who is in you is greater than him (see 1 John 4:4) and holds the keys of death and hell (see Revelation 1:18). If you are in Christ, you fight from a position of victory because He has won the ultimate victory! Have you lost your will to fight? I realize that this might be counter-intuitive to the way you were brought up, but eventually, you are going to have to pull your pants up, jump into the heat of the battle and wage war. Your participation is required. There are no exemptions. Your skinny jeans might split, and your fake nails fall off, but you are called to this fight. Ask any athlete. The joy is in playing the game. The possibility of winning or losing is the reason why they get up every day and put in the work. They know gameday is coming. They will soon be thrust into the battlefield of uncertainty where all they have prepared for will be put to the test. And so will you. Your battle is coming. Are you prepared? Are you hoping that someone else will fight for you? They can't! Your parent's faith or lack of faith is not enough to help you in this fight. Your kids can't help you. Your friends can't go with you. Your giant is your giant. You are going to have to face it head-on. You already have what you need inside of you. The gifts, resources, and grace have already been given to you by God to fight with. You have to use them. See yourself as enough. Throw what you know at your giant! God is throwing with you!

WHY?

These have come so that the proven genuineness of your faith—of greater worth than gold, which perishes even though refined by fire—may result in praise, glory and honor when Jesus Christ is revealed.

1 Peter 1:7 (NIV)

"Why?" is a question that is often brought up when we don't understand something or what is going on in our life. It is normal for us to question and even investigate the reasons why something is the way it is. It is that desire to know that often leads to our biggest self-discoveries and breakthroughs. About eight years ago, I collapsed on my driveway. I was under a tremendous amount of pressure, and my back just gave out. In truth, I had been feeling some discomfort for a little while, and this wasn't the first time I had been laid up in bed because of my back. This time was different, though. I had enough! I could sense that God also had had enough of me walking around the same mountains. It was time for a change. He was trying to get my attention, and this seemed the only way that He could get it. This breaking point was a blessing as it started me on my journey toward emotional health. It led my wife and me to start our own business, C3 Athletics (as mentioned earlier), a health and fitness company. I had always been an athlete. I was active and loved it, but the demands of life had corroded that priority. Not anymore. I discovered some things about myself that needed to be addressed. This wasn't just about my physical health. God was going to work on the *total* me. I was strong physically, but not where it mattered most. There were parts of me that were undeveloped and neglected. I was going to have to get serious about strengthening my foundation if I was going to be able to hold all that God was calling me into. My core. The inner part of who I was needed rehab. There were parts of this process that helped realign me and reintroduce me to some key components to load-bearing exercises. More on this later. I was strong but couldn't stabilize very well. This lack of stability caused me to overcompensate with other muscles, and as a result, over time, these muscles never really developed. I had to learn to rebuild strength in the unseen areas, so I could hold the weight of the intensity of the workouts I was putting my body through. Over time I got stronger. But it did not come without pain. This is where the struggle is for most people. They want magic pills but not the process. The quick fix, but not the slow climb of change. Lasting change. I eventually progressed to the point where I was regularly involved in HITT (high-intensity interval training) and CrossFit workouts. This change opened the door not only to my physical health but to my emotional and spiritual health as well. I realized that there is a correlation between all three. When I prioritize my physical health, it helps my emotional capacity as I start to feel better about myself and the way I look at life. My spiritual understanding also broadens as I come into a better understanding of God's design for my life as a whole person. By connecting to who I am, I come into a broader understanding of God. Breaking was a blessing as it gave me an opportunity to heal. When God gets ready to promote you, He will peek into some of the closets of your inner house to make sure they are not filled with unnecessary clutter. He will go to work to clean house, to make sure He has enough room to move in. He will go to work in the unseen to build in you the iron you need to withstand the pressure that comes along with your purpose. You *have* a purpose. It is not until you are forced to slow down that you begin to take inventory of how you fit into that purpose. To see what has fallen behind the shelf or been misplaced due to a lack of understanding. Looking into the closets of your life allows you to see how far you have come and what needs to be moved or thrown out. It is a blessing for you to go through an internal audit so God can rework and move some of your old files to the recycle bin. To empty the trash from your old life and start fresh again. Many of you who are reading this book may be in a similar position. You're running on empty. Trying to draw strength from a part of you that is either dead or not developed. You're trying to avoid the inevitable, hoping that no one sees, but all signs point to a crash. More work isn't going to fix it. Pretending that it's not there is not going to make it go away. You must own up to it. You must engage until failure. You will then be able to see what needs to be fixed and allow God to reset what has been broken. Hesitation can be your biggest enemy in this process as you will undoubtedly be confronted with the questions of *"Why me?" "Why am I going through this?"* It will be a hurdle that you will continually have to jump over if you are going to see the finish line. Let me help you with that thought process. You're not the only one! The enemy would like nothing more for you to think that you are an exception and that no one is going through what you're going through. He's a liar. I don't care if you are the CEO of a Fortune 500 company or a maid. Behind every face are the inner workings of the Maker who is hammering at the fabric of His creation, molding them into His image. I mentioned earlier that I started getting into CrossFit. My first introduction to CrossFit was Murph:

1-mile run

100 pullups

200 pushups

300 air squats

1-mile run

My wife invited me out to a WOD ("Workout of the Day") on Memorial Day in 2013. Keep in mind that my wife had already been bitten by the CrossFit bug and had gotten her Level 1 certification. She had failed to mention what Murph was, and I was too naive to know any different. I was an athlete. How bad could it be? I realized quickly when I started the run that I wasn't going to last very long. At that time, I wasn't really a runner and could relate more to Gimli from Lord of The Rings, The Two Towers (2002), "*I'm wasted on cross-country! We dwarves are natural sprinters! Very dangerous over short distances!*" Moving into the next phase, I started my ring rows (a modification from pull-ups). As I started, my fight or flight response kicked in and I "flighted" passing out. They told me that I hit my head on a pole. I don't really remember! Lol. Lack of conditioning, dehydration, and a lack of pacing led to my demise that day. However, that experience woke me up, and I vowed to get better. I did not want to miss out on doing hard things just because it was uncomfortable or pushed me to the end of myself. I realized that my journey wasn't going to be easy, but it would be worth the climb.

This mindset translates to your emotional health as well. What is taxing you emotionally, draining you of your ability to cope with the pressures of life? Have you checked out of the process? Do you need to make an adjustment to the way you look at things? Pressure is a privilege. It causes you to dig deep to find solutions to problems and bring out the best part of you that is hidden beneath comfortability. You are a better version of yourself when you are under pressure. God can get to the best parts of you when you are pressed. Some of you might be thinking I do everything to avoid pressure, and I hate confrontation. How are you living? Pressure is what God uses! He will thrust you into situations where your faith will be tested, and the underlying issues that are affecting your emotions can be dealt with.

I was one of the many over the past two years to get COVID. I woke up Christmas day 2020 feeling absolutely awful. After I put a hole in my mother-in-law's wall while riding my daughter's hoverboard, I found myself on the couch, exhausted and weary. After taking my temperature, I had a fever. This cut the Christmas festivities short for me as I headed home to sleep. Three days later, I took a COVID test, and it came back negative. I thought it was a bad flu and that I had escaped its clutches. Little did I know of the impending "doom" I would soon experience. For eight straight days, I had a fever that would not break. On the eighth day, my body had enough. I collapsed in the shower from exhaustion, thrusting my wife and family into panic mode. My wife called EMS. I was able to dress myself and make my way downstairs before they put me on the gurney. Upon arrival at the hospital, they took my vitals and gave me a COVID test. It not only came back positive, but I also found out that I had an infection, double pneumonia, and was dehydrated. Remarkably, I never lost taste and smell. What a day! I was admitted and stayed one night in the hospital, hooked up to an IV so I could get fluids and meds. The next day I woke up with a determination that I was not going to stay in the hospital longer than I had to. There was no shower, and the room was small. With a small white towel, oxygen in my nose, and an IV in my arm, I started working out. The doctors eventually walked in and asked me how I was doing and what I was doing. I told them, and they were shocked. They said they had not seen this before from a COVID patient before. They asked me if I wanted to go home and of course, I said *yes*! I called my wife, and she was shocked. Originally, the charge nurse said that I would have to stay in the hospital for a week. But God! They sent me home with my oxygen level in the high 80s and with meds. I felt like death and looked like death, but at least I could heal at home.

We are faced with many trials in life. A trial can be defined as a tryout or experiment to test quality, value, or usefulness. (Merriam-Webster, n.d) They are sent to test us. Their objective is to teach us how to persevere as we are becoming the men and women God envisioned we would be. Consider this story about the Silver Smith:

There was once a group of women studying the book of Malachi in the Old Testament. As they were studying chapter three, they came across verse three, which says: "He will sit as a refiner and purifier of silver." This verse puzzled the women, and they wondered what this statement meant about the character and nature of God. One of the women offered to find out about the process of refining silver and get back to the group at their next Bible study.

That week this woman called up a silversmith and made an appointment to watch him at work. She didn't mention anything about the reason for her interest beyond her curiosity about the process of refining silver. As she watched the silversmith, he held a piece of silver over the fire and let it heat up. He explained that in refining silver, one needed to hold the silver in the middle of the fire where the flames were hottest so as to burn away all the impurities.

The woman thought about God holding us in such a hot spot. Then she thought again about the verse, that he sits as a refiner and purifier of silver. She asked the silversmith if it was true that he had to sit there in front of the fire the whole time the silver was being refined.

The man answered, "Yes," and explained that he not only had to sit there holding the silver, but he had to keep his eyes on the silver the entire time it was in the fire. If the silver was left even a moment too long in the flames, it would be damaged. The woman was silent for a moment. Then she asked the silversmith, "How do you know when the silver is fully refined?"

He smiled at her and answered, "Oh, that's easy. When I see my image in it."

So, what is God looking for in the trial? Himself! Are you becoming more like Him? Your faith, like a seed planted in good soil, is given the opportunity to grow in inclement weather. It must be exercised and develop a strong root system. Watered by difficulty and exposed to heat, your faith is given the necessary fuel that allows you to weather life's storms. Storms are coming! If you don't have a strong enough root system, you will wither under the pressure of the storm. The storm will bring you out of hiding and chasten you. They are unavoidable! There is no relationship, job, or possession that can hide you from it.

As you are tried, your belief system will undergo intense scrutiny as to its validity, and what you've heard your whole life will be called into question and interrogated. If you're not careful, you can mistake the storm for God's disappointment, but if you see with eyes of faith, you can view it as discipline motivated by love:

> *But God disciplines us for our good, in order that we may share in his holiness. No discipline seems pleasant at the time, but painful. Later on, however, it produces a harvest of righteousness and peace for those who have been trained by it.*
>
> **Hebrews 12:10–11 (NIV)**

You might be thinking, *I never liked discipline*. Who did? It never felt good, but the intention behind it was your growth. God sees you as a son or daughter. He loves you enough to discipline you and bring you into full maturity. He doesn't just invite you to salvation but to a process of sanctification. Sanctification is a process that takes a lifetime and involves the stripping away of your old self and renovation of your thoughts and behaviors.

It's Time

> *When I was a child, I spoke and thought and reasoned as a child. But when I grew up, I put away childish things.*
>
> **1 Corinthians 13:11 (NLT)**

God wants you to grow up. Like a father who puts his kids in the best environments to grow, God will put you in the best classrooms of life so you can thrive. He knows how to challenge you in order to get you to reach your potential. I don't care what kind of environment you grew up in or what you think you missed; God can bring out of you what others failed to develop in you. As Headmaster, He has orchestrated your life and the difficulties that you have encountered to bring you to the place you are at now. He knows the answers to the tests and how you will respond. Your faith will bring you through the test quicker. He will keep giving you the tests until you've learned what you need to learn. I call it the Boomerang Effect. That one thing that keeps coming around to you, testing your response. It is your response to the testing that tells the story of your progress.

Recidivism is a term used to describe a tendency to relapse into a previous condition or mode of behavior. (Merriam-Webster, n.d.)

If your response to the test is to bolt because it's too hard or you're not a good test taker, you forfeit the opportunity to pass, delaying your graduation to the next level. There are no excuses when it comes to taking the tests. Everyone is tested, and there are different versions of tests. They are tailored just for you. Cheating is not an option. Calling in sick is not an option. Consequently, If you can take the pressure that comes along with taking the test and still take the test, you build character and are taught lessons that will guide you through the various roads that life is going to take you on. God knows the roads that are ahead of you and how you are going to get there. If you can hold up under the tension of an ambiguous outcome, you stretch your capacity to hold more and graduate from the rudimentary principles of life into advanced Christianity. If your response to difficulty is to end up in a fetal position with your thumb in your mouth, then you know you still are *acting like a child* and have not *put away childish things.* If the strip club is still an option when your wife or husband does not satisfy your needs, then you still are *acting like a child* and have not *put away childish things.* I can't tell you how many times manhood has presented itself in the form of a problem that I needed to face. Running from it would have been easier but not beneficial. That's what boys do. Facing it was the solution to defeating the boyish tendencies of "when I was a child." It was the very thing I needed to hurdle and helped cut the umbilical cord that tied me to boyhood.

Why is God's discipline essential? There are so many who are running around spiritually parched, seeking the springs of life that can only come from the Giver of life. Longing for fulfillment, they drink from cups that are half-filled and rarely satisfy. They bounce from relationship to relationship, trying to fill the void that only a relationship with Jesus Christ can fill. Secretly, they long for solace, a place to be accepted for who they are, but outwardly they are too afraid to voice their need, fearing rejection or ostracization. Or worse, being canceled! This new cancel culture has wreaked havoc on the social fabric of our society, tearing away at an already fragile foundation.

Accountability has given way to lawlessness. Trust has given way to cynicism. In the name of tolerance, sacred traditional views of marriage and relationships are under attack. Children are being taught to explore and question their sexuality at a young age. They are presented with pictures that call into question their own identity and are left to struggle with the questions of right and wrong. What is supposed to be normal is now looked at with skepticism as more and more people are becoming "woke." Woke to what? Racial injustice? Yes. Cultural norms? Yes. But I think it's more than that. People are becoming increasingly aware of their need for a higher truth, and in their outcries, they are revealing their real need. A need for a Savior. Someone to fix what is broken. Trying to intellectualize or explain away real-world problems doesn't fix the fact that we are broke; broke in our system of government, broke in our emotions, and broke in our ideals. We have drifted away from those ideals that made this nation "one nation under God." No nation is perfect, and no nation is without a history that preceded it. More government programs are not going to fix the torn psyche of our nation. We have fallen in love with our own intellect and ability to reason that we have forgotten what has made this nation a great nation. We need real solutions that don't handicap our progress, take away our liberties, and force us into dependency. Real solutions empower individuals to take control of their lives, giving them the ability to choose. We were created to be free with the ability to self-govern and the right to choose. Co-dependency robs people of self-discovery and creativity. It forces people to stay trapped in an endless cycle of feeding dysfunction, stifling their progress. Are you co-dependent? How do you know if you're co-dependent? If your survival is based upon what fix you need next, you're co-dependent. If you have to wait on someone else's approval before you make a decision, you're co-dependent. Co-dependency is a cancer that erodes self-worth and cripples your ability to flourish. You need a power source greater than you if you are going to unravel its grip on your life. You need a Savior!

God will deal with you in stages. He doesn't perfect you all at once. Like dough that is needed, pounded, and stretched, He prepares you to serve. Like a good chef, He already knows what the finished product should be like. He sees you tomorrow! He knows how long each season of your life will be and when the final bell will ring, signifying your graduation from this life.

For we are God's handiwork, created in Christ Jesus to do good works, which God prepared in advance for us to do.
Ephesians 2:10 (NIV)

God already has planned good works for you to walk in. It's only a matter of time before He will get you to them. While you are waiting, He is preparing you and those around you to walk in them. This is not an idle wait. It is an active move from what you know on your way to what you don't know. This is an important principle to understand, and where people get tripped up, misunderstanding God's role in the process. God will not do everything for you.

His grace will draw you, but He will allow you to search for Him and His will through the various circumstances that come into your life. Remember, this is a walk with God. The joy is in getting to know Him and His ways in the process. Through a series of ill-timed (according to us) and unforeseen events, we are thrust into the fires of testing, where we are presented with the choice to seek God or die. Regardless of what you have heard from your Sunday school teacher, the struggle is real. These are tests! If you want to pass, you must exercise your faith. There have been times in my life when I have been presented with the option to tap out, but His grace gave me the strength to keep saying yes to His will.

I can remember coming off a very difficult season of my life. We had just finished a grueling season of ministry and were asked to be part of another church staff. It wasn't unfamiliar territory, as I had grown up and worked at the church that we were interviewing at. Looking back, it was a struggle! I had to wrestle through thoughts of doubt in my mind as to me I would be going "backward." The position would require me to oversee less than what I was previously over, and after much prayer, I knew it was where God wanted me to be. It was a time to heal and get a fresh vision for our future.

It was apparent that God had other plans for me than just a quick trip down memory lane. He began to separate me from my family of origin and start to go to work on the inner boy that needed to heal from his past. I had been abused as a kid, and unbeknown to me, the lingering effects of that abuse, as well as other emotional issues, were still lurking in the inner recesses of my heart. I was stuck. Unable to properly process these emotions, I ended up going through some much-needed counseling to help reframe and restore who I was. Most of my teenage years were spent in unhealthy relationships that overshadowed my worth and significance. There were things that were brought to light about my identity that I had not dealt with. The busyness of ministry had concealed these wounds that were infiltrating my self-worth.

Our family had moved down from New York in 1987. My dad and a friend he knew went into business and opened a Christian bookstore called Glorybound Christian Bookstore. It was exciting at first as it was something we had never done before. Excitement turned to disappointment, though, as we soon realized that my dad's business partner had taken him for a lot of money, causing us to file bankruptcy. This did not bode well for a family of six at the time with four kids under the age of eleven. Of course, I took it the hardest as I had a front-row seat to what I would call our undoing. I began to question the validity of our move. Did we leave New York for this? Frustration turned to anger as I soon realized that our house with a pool and garage, along with our new cars, would become a thing of the past. The seven of us (yes, my dad and mom were now expecting another child) moved into a three-bedroom/two-bath apartment.

We were left with Frank and Betsy, two old cars that we named because of their lackluster appearance and that you could hear and spot coming down the road from a mile away. Betsy was an old grey station wagon with a red interior and back seat that faced outward to the world and the drivers behind us. To add insult to injury, the back of the station wagon made a loud noise so you could hear us coming down the street! To a teenager, this was grounds for social ostracization. We were mortified. Frank was an orange Cadillac with a loose interior ceiling liner that would rain down brown dirt on you when you were in the car. You could also carve your initials and write on the interior of the car with your finger.

I was introduced to lack at a young age. It was a rude awakening. Having to search for answers, I was left to try and sort through the emotional toll of loss. Why would God move us to Florida only to have us lose everything? Playing the church game, I drifted most of my teenage years spiritually, never really committing fully to Christ.

After high school, I went to the University of South Florida. I can remember sitting in my dorm during the spring semester of my freshman year, and that familiar voice that I had heard speak before broke through all the noise. I felt that still, small voice say, "It's time to go back home and do what I've called you to do." I had given my heart over to Jesus at eleven but did not really understand the gravity of what that meant. Through all my drifting and outward show, God's hand was still on my life. At age nineteen, He knew that there was a boy inside who needed an overhaul. I answered the call to go back and ended up finishing my associate's degree at St. Petersburg

College. I then enrolled in Countryside Christian Training Center, where I got my Associate of Ministerial Studies. Eventually, I would finish my bachelor's, master's, and a doctorate in Sacred Studies at Christian Life School of Theology.

Leave

If you are going to expect to get anywhere with God, you won't be able to stay where you have always been. When God is ready to start something new, He will ask you to leave what you are familiar with to step into the unknown. It's where He likes to hang out.

Look at what He asked Abram to do in Genesis 12:

The Lord had said to Abram,
"Go from your country, your people and your father's
household to the land I will show you.
"I will make you into a great nation,
and I will bless you;
I will make your name great,
and you will be a blessing.
I will bless those who bless you,
and whoever curses you I will curse;
and all peoples on earth
will be blessed through you."

Genesis 12:1–3 (NIV)

We used to sing a song growing up in Kids Church about Abraham…

Father Abraham had many sons, and many sons had

Father Abraham. I am one of them, and so are you. So, let's just praise the Lord. It was a reminder of what one man's obedience did to change the trajectory of our faith and unlock the blessings that, as Christians, we are experiencing today.

Your obedience will change the trajectory of your faith and the trajectory of those that are coming behind you. Are you looking for a change? More importantly, is God asking something of you that will require you to change? Our willingness to go and do what He asks us to do, despite the unknown variables and what we must leave behind, opens the doors to His blessings in our life. There are many who want to find out what God's will is but aren't willing to adjust their course. They are still concerned with security and want guarantees. There is no security apart from God. The guarantee? The guarantee is that He will never leave you or forsake you (see Hebrews 13:5). To Him, He is enough. We have to change our thinking from Jesus and…to Jesus alone. So, how do we start?

Check out **Romans 12:2 (NIV)**:

Do not conform to the pattern of this world, but be transformed by the renewing of your mind. Then you will be able to test and approve what God's will is – his good, pleasing and perfect will.

Conform comes from the Greek word *to identify with.* (Bible Hub, n.d.) We are born into a world that assigns us a social security number. It signifies that we are a citizen—a citizen of the state that we were born in. That number is used to identify us, especially when applying for jobs, credit, and allows us to travel. It gives us access to a world of possibilities. Conformity carries over into our life as we grow. We are introduced as John's kid, or "that's Richie's daughter." We learn to take sides and identify as belonging to a specific party or group. We fall in love with a particular brand or style (just look back at your teenage and young adult pictures). We are conditioned to want to fit. Don't think so? Take a look at social media. Selfies dominate posts. Likes rule. Dislikes create tension. Everyone wants affirmation. It is a core need that must be met. However, if done in an unhealthy way, it can lead you into places that you don't want to be. Physical abuse, sexual exploitation, and misappropriation of affections are all results of affirmation "gone bad." It is a sickness in our society that needs to be addressed. We are enamored with bigger and better, conforming to what we possess as opposed to identifying with *Who* possesses us. Have you fallen into that trap? Have you ever stopped to think that conformity is robbing you of your self-worth? Have you ever stopped to question the "rules?" Pushed back on ideological norms? Challenged the status quo? This is the juxtaposition that comes with following Jesus and living in a fallen world. He makes it difficult for you to identify with the world. He will interrupt the norm and challenge your ideals and traditions. The way He sees it and the way you see it will clash. His thoughts on particular issues and the way He works will conflict with yours. Here are three things that God will interfere with:

Humanism

An outlook or system of thought attaching prime importance to human rather than divine or supernatural matters. (Dictionary, n.d.) Humanists place a high value on the goodness of mankind. God recognizes the need for mankind to be redeemed. That's why He came. There is a difference between being a religious person and having a relationship with God. Religion says, "How can I get to God?" God says, "I'll come to you." Religion emphasizes good works. God says your works are like filthy rags (see Isaiah 64:6).

Idolatry

Putting it simply, anything that you exalt above God. This can be an attitude, a relationship, or something that you possess. God told the Israelites in Exodus 20:3, "... *you shall have no other gods before me.*" We are stewards of what has been given to us by Him. Placing those things above God gives way to the worship of those things. Our time, talents, and treasure: all belong to Him. What you do with them reflects your attitude toward the One who gave them to you.

Perversion

They are many forms of perversion. In short, perversion is taking what is natural and twisting it to satisfy an inner craving. It is a result of depravity and a lack of adherence to biblical standards. The reality is that there is an aching in your soul that needs to be satisfied. But it cannot be satisfied by taking something that God has called good and perverting it. Sexual immorality is a problem that God deals with…

So God abandoned them to do whatever shameful things their hearts desired. As a result, they did vile and degrading things with each other's bodies.
Romans 1:24 (NLT)

Perversion is a tactic of the enemy. He will use it to twist people's emotions and bring them into bondage. It is not until you have been bound by something do you see the need for freedom. After you have gone a few rounds in life, you quickly realize that people can't give you fulfillment in the way that God can. You can keep searching for significance in the lap of your best friend or mate, but you will leave empty as they were never designed to fill your cup to overflowing like God can. So many people are leaking from their souls, hemorrhaging their needs onto other people, expecting them to meet them. They are not rooted in the One who is the true *Source* of life. Can this change? Yes, but it doesn't come without transformation. The word transformed from Romans 12:2 comes from the Greek word *meta*, which means *"change after being with."* (Bible Hub, n.d.) You remember growing up and hearing you will become like who you run with. It's true. Ask any mother or father who has had their son or daughter disappear into the shadows to find themselves. It is a lonely experience to have to navigate as the search for significance can be long and daunting. Parents, you have a responsibility to raise your kids with a healthy sense of self-worth. If the question of "*Who am I?*" remains unanswered, it will result in someone or something filling in the blank. If you don't help them fill in the blank, there are plenty of gangs and predators who are happy to assist. Why is this important? Because if you can't define who you are, someone else will! If you are not anchored in your true identity, it is easier to be pulled in directions that you don't want to go, resulting in change that you really don't want to see. Sex changes are not going to fix what is broken. Trying on different versions of sexuality is not going to make the uneasiness inside go away or validate the "that's just who I am" argument. The tension will remain. Is it possible to reverse the stigma of a distorted view of sexual orientation? Yes, only through renewing. The word *renewing* means a *renewal or change of heart and life that can only be achieved by God's power*. (Bible Hub, n.d.) Those struggling with sexual identity issues don't need another inclusive message or group supporting their lifestyle. They need an understanding of God's love for them. He is the only One that can break them free from that chain.

Get in the Pool

In **John 5:1–9 (NKJV)**, we see a story of a man who was healed of an infirmity that he had for thirty-eight years.

After this there was a feast of the Jews, and Jesus went

up to Jerusalem. Now there is in Jerusalem by the Sheep Gate a pool, which is called in Hebrew, Bethesda, having five porches. In these lay a great multitude of sick people, blind, lame, paralyzed, waiting for the moving of the water. For an angel went down at a certain time into the pool and stirred up the water; then whoever stepped in first, after the stirring of the water, was made well of whatever disease he had. Now a certain man was there who had an infirmity thirty-eight years. When Jesus saw him lying there, and knew that he already had been in that condition a long time, He said to him, "Do you want to be made well?"

The sick man answered Him, "Sir, I have no man to put me into the pool when the water is stirred up; but while I am coming, another steps down before me."

Jesus said to him, "Rise, take up your bed and walk." And immediately the man was made well, took up his bed, and walked. And that day was the Sabbath.

We are not told how he got the infirmity, but what matters is how long he remained in this condition. Year after year, he saw others get healed. You would think that at some point he would have stayed near the pool to get first dibs when the angel stirred the water. It's not like he wasn't able to come down, for the Bible says in verse 7:

The sick man answered Him, "Sir, I have no man to put me into the pool when the water is stirred up; but while I am coming, another steps down before me."

Sadly, many who are crippled by disappointment in life stay that way. Unable to climb out of their own way, they stay conformed to where they grew up, how they were raised, and what happened to them. Rather than do the hard work of "getting out" or getting better, they resort to unhealthy behaviors that lead to addiction and loss. They are victims. And everyone knows that they are victims. They have bought into the lie that there is no way out. Pain and self-doubt are their only allies, and they are left panhandling for a way to just through life. They are waiting on someone to rescue them. In truth, they have the power to change their position and to take steps toward a better life. I am aware that there are people who are physically and mentally confined due to their condition and unable to make necessary changes for themselves. But there are others who are capable of moving positions in their life but are too lazy to do the work necessary. Idleness is their comfort, and they lack the urgency to change and end up dying a slow death due to inactivity. They are stuck in the regrets of yesterday, and their will to live has been replaced with the "what ifs" or "so whats" of tomorrow. This is a travesty! There is a difference between being sidelined for a season and being sidelined for most of your life, never coming out of the shadows because you are afraid of getting hurt again. It's time to live! To pull the shades up and let the light in again. We have all had tragedy strike, but it's how you look at and respond to it that matters.

Are you waiting on someone else to rescue you? They are not coming! If you want to be made well, you are going to have to go for yourself. You are going to have to do the work to put yourself in a position to receive what Jesus died to give you. Notice what I said, do the work, and put yourself in a position to receive. There is not some magic pill or fairy dust that is going to make your problems disappear. This is life! You were never promised a life free from trouble.

Jesus tells us in **John 16:33 (NIV)**:

"I have told you these things, so that in me you may have peace. In this world you will have trouble. But take heart! I have overcome the world."

The problem that many we have today is that we have a "handout" and "feed me" mentality. We are consumers, especially when it comes to spirituality. We're waiting on somebody or some leader to give us what we need. *If I can just hear a word from him or get him to pray for me, then things will change.* Here is the word for you: *Get up and start walking again!* God will begin to direct your steps. While people can offer some wisdom and guidance and spur you on to good works (see Hebrews 10:24), they can't fix you. Therapists and counselors can validate your feelings and attempt to regulate your emotions, but they can't transform your life. You need Someone who can get down in the hard-to-reach broken places of your life and reset them. You need Jesus! We are all broken. That's why Jesus came. Notice what Jesus said to this man in *verse 6:*

When Jesus saw him lying there and knew that he already had been in that condition a long time, He said to him, "Do you want to be made well?"

John 5:6 (NKJV)

This is a loaded question. "Isn't it obvious, man? Yeah, I want to be made well." Is it, though? You have been lying here in your own feces for a long time. I realize that we are talking about a physical infirmity here, but the question applies to your particular affliction as well. Whether it be emotionally, mentally, or even financially, Jesus presents us with the same question. As a sidebar, I'm not here to debate the open-ended question of why some people get healed and others don't. Ultimately, God is in control and has the final say. But the fact that Jesus stops to address this particular individual illuminates the importance of this question. There is something inherently wrong with the unwillingness to change even though you know that you have to. Pain and rejection will force you into one of two places: immobility or mobility. Immobility, by closing you off to better. Mobility, by allowing the pain or rejection to thrust you into God's purpose. Closed doors are just as essential as opened ones. If you can see others' rejection as God's protection, you will move quickly through the pain of a break into healing. Are you here? Has Jesus stopped by your house and asked you the question, "Do you want to be made well?" What are you bumping up against that has paralyzed you? Is it a lost relationship? Someone you thought was going to be with you until the end, but they have decided to look elsewhere? Are you in a relationship that has become a burden to you? Are you unequally yoked? Tied to someone who does not hold the same values as you? Are you blaming God for your circumstances? I am convinced that most of what we deal with is a result of who or what we connect ourselves to and the unrealistic expectations that we assign to them. If we are unwilling to extinguish the toxic environments that we run in, then we will always reek of the flames of defeat. We can't fall in love with crazy and expect that somehow crazy is going to change. If it looks like a duck and quacks like a duck, it's a duck. If you are being checked in your spirit by the Spirit of God regarding your relationships, listen. There is no shame in calling off an engagement or ending a relationship if it is not God's will for you. Others can talk about it with their friends, coworkers can gossip about it, and parents can grieve the loss, but they eventually will get over it. Your peace is worth the break. There are many who have ignored those checks only to find out later that their partner was really a poser. Reality shows are filled with posers trying to find love. If you must go on national TV to find your soul mate, then you have bigger issues that need to be dealt with. Dysfunction is not funny! Want a healthy relationship? Get in the community and find someone who holds similar values, complements you, and doesn't control you. You will put yourself in a position to succeed and give yourself a better chance at winning in life. Take inventory of your relationships. Are the victims—those with a victim mentality—monopolizing your time and slowing you down? Push them to Christ. You don't have time to be someone else's crutch. Eventually, the weight will be too much for you to bear. "Do you want to be made well?" If yes, then you must be willing to make the necessary adjustments to allow the healing to take place. Most people want better, but there always seems to be a "but" that gets in their way. Change is hard and requires the symbiotic relationship of our mind, will, and emotions. This man's condition gives us a deeper look into that process. What are you sick of? You can't afford another year of no change. Why not make a declaration that this year will be greater than last year? Yes, despite the incredulous rhetoric coming from those around you, stand up. Take your life back! Breathe again! Reintroduce yourself to the world. Make a decision that you are not going to live sidelined by something that you really had no control over. If you need inspiration, watch the Paralympics. It is a fascinating display of grit and guts as participants with physical and mental disabilities compete against one another. It is a picture of people playing free. Control is an illusion. To think that somehow you could have avoided how things turned out in your life is misguided. You are not in control. Life is subject to change at any moment. You don't get to pick the instruments that God uses to work out His ultimate purpose. Are you still waiting on that apology that might never come? Or for an explanation as to why your life turned out the way it did? Are you harboring bitterness toward someone who left you a long time ago? The power of moving on is in the ability for you to release that person or expectation to God and start to move forward. Your life is too short for you to stay on hold over something that you probably should have gotten over a long time ago. Can I propose a different solution? Allow God to take you to the place where you got stuck. Process through the pain and disappointment with a counselor or friend. You were meant for more than just rehearsing old tapes of regret in your head. Until you get sick of hearing that same tape in your head, it will continue to dictate what you do with your life. Stand up to your own head! Make a declaration to yourself that your past will *not* define you. Get around a community of people who will push you to change. Take the limits off yourself and allow accountability to be a footstool that you stand on so you can make it through to the other side of better. Give yourself a chance to win by breaking the cycle of inferiority and inadequacy in your life. As a personal trainer, I come across people with different goals and limitations. Most people who are overweight complain that their back hurts and that they must modify an exercise so they can complete it. Here's the truth: lose the weight, strengthen your core, and you'll start to see a change in how you look and feel. And yes, watch what you eat! You can't continue to work on one component and neglect the other. There needs to be a symbiotic relationship on all levels if you are going to see transformation. I'm not talking about kale and vegetables-only diet, but structure your diet in such a way that allows you "cheat days" without cheating your progress. Why is this important? One of the most frustrating things is when something that was designed to work is not working as it should. Take your computer, for example. It is a great feeling when you pull a new Mac laptop (sorry, Windows users) out of the box and start using it. The computer is outfitted with the necessary RAM and applications needed to make the computer run effectively. Like most, you end up downloading additional programs and applications as needed that fit your needs. However, temp files and scripts are downloaded with those applications and end up taking up space on your hard drive, slowing down the speed of your computer. Slowly, you end up overloading your computer, and it starts to run sluggishly, resulting in that wonderful spinning colorful pinwheel. Other times, the problem is the applications or programs that are running in the background that we forget to close out! What is running in the background of your life right now? What scripts from your past are dictating the narrative of your life today? You know the nagging lines that tell you will always be this way. You'll never change. You'll always be overweight. You'll always crack under pressure because you are not strong enough. You'll never be in a healthy relationship. Who would want to love you? You were born a nobody, and you'll die a nobody. It always ends badly for you. What makes you think this time will be any different? Sound familiar? So many are letting their yesterday define their tomorrow. They listen to the same songs every day. Like a broken record player that keeps repeating, they are stuck in a cycle of rehashing old wounds, regrets, and missed opportunities. They are hobbling through life, medicating themselves with quick fixes and solvents, hoping to find relief, too afraid to admit they are falling apart inside and that they have given up on the hope of a better future.

I can't help but think of how many times better has presented itself in the form of a friend, a new job, or a venture. But because it required leaving an unhealthy relationship, transferring to another state, or restarting, many have missed out on what could have been the start of a better life. They have settled for a life of mediocrity. There is something to be said about being comfortable with dysfunction. Too many have made their bed in that world and accepted it as normal. They have bought a house there and put down roots making it their forever home.

ORIGINAL INTENT

God blessed them and said to them, "Be fruitful and increase in number; fill the earth and subdue it. Rule over the fish in the sea and the birds in the sky and over every living creature that moves on the ground."

Genesis 1:28 (NIV)

God's original intent was for man to be fruitful and subdue the earth. We were meant to rule. The Garden is man's first class on "ruling 101." It is there that they meet the antagonist of this story, Satan, who takes on the form of a serpent and broaches the subject of God's original instructions to Adam and Eve. He is also a created being who had already failed at his assignment.

Now the serpent was more crafty than any of the wild animals the Lord God had made. He said to the woman, "Did God really say, 'You must not eat from any tree in the garden'?" The woman said to the serpent, "We may eat fruit from the trees in the garden, but God did say, 'You must not eat fruit

from the tree that is in the middle of the garden, and you must not touch it, or you will die.'"
Genesis 3:1–3 (NIV)

Having lost his highest position in heaven because of His pride, Lucifer now comes in the form of a serpent to tempt Adam and Eve to disobey God. It is one of his oldest tricks; to try and get you to doubt God and what He has already spoken to you about. Unfortunately, Adam and Eve took the bait:

When the woman saw that the fruit of the tree was good for food and pleasing to the eye, and also desirable for gaining wisdom, she took some and ate it. She also gave some to her husband, who was with her, and he ate it. Then the eyes of both of them were opened, and they realized they were naked; so they sewed fig leaves together and made coverings for themselves.
Genesis 3:6–7 (NIV)

Their eyes were open. Their innocence—lost. Their true identity—stripped. They failed the test of obedience thrusting mankind into the clutches of sin. Sin (separation from God) and its partner death now make their entrance onto the world's stage. Purpose will help you avoid the traps of pleasure. It will guide you along the right paths, picking the fruit that is best for you. No one likes rotten fruit, but so many pick off the trees of spoiled and outdated methods that never deliver on their promise to satisfy. You are enriched by what you take in. In other words, you are what you eat. There is nothing wrong with enjoying the good things that life has to offer. However, enjoying life doesn't mean leaving God. Even greener pastures still have brown underneath. You can have a relationship with God and still enjoy life. I would propose that you can't have one without the other. Too many try to experience life without God and are ensnared by their own cravings. Unable to shake the buzz of sexual promiscuity or emotional misconduct, they dig holes for themselves that are too deep for them to climb out of. Because they are never truly filled, they continue to dig, making the climb out that much harder. They are never satisfied. It is exhausting to try and keep up the filling process so you can feel good about yourself. Only God can fill that space inside you that you are looking for someone or something to fill. What have you said "yes" to that is secretly killing you? The one thing that is eroding your identity and twisting your emotions so you can't see straight? Opening the doors to perversion will cloud your senses when it comes to intimacy. The teleprompter in your head has a long memory bank. It will continually scroll through vivid images of past sexual encounters that will pervert your ability to see love in its purest form. Or, perhaps you are one of the many who are sexually active because, hey, everyone is doing it, and after all, you have needs. Along with being sexually active, you must take into consideration the emotional component of sex that will break you down if you are not ready for it. Every encounter brings with it a soul tie that is carried onto the next relationship. Eventually, if you get married, you are bringing those encounters with you to the bedroom, where comparison and expectation play their game. Guilt and shame are big players on that field. Intimacy (In-to-Me-See) is the goal in relationships, not sex. Countless men and women are using each other for sex, thinking that there will be no consequences. Ask the individuals who have contracted HIV or herpes if there are no consequences. Listen to the commercials that describe the drugs that have been created to help those who have contracted a disease "to cope." The side effects are more numerous than the benefits! There is no such thing as casual sex. Friends with benefits are still friends who are sexually involved. Students and young adults have learned this hard way resulting in countless babies being born out of wedlock. There are plenty of kids running around with parents who have had their kids "by accident." Still wanting to live their lives, they cast their kids aside because they just want to have fun. You lost a "you first" mentality when you found out you were having a kid. By accident or not, you now are responsible to do what is in the best interests of that kid. If you're not ready for the responsibility that comes along with being sexually active—don't! Your "oops" can cause some major problems for you, especially if you don't even like the person you were sexually active with. Wait until you find a partner that has been called alongside you to do life with. It will save you from comparing your previous encounters with the one who is now with you.

Hide and Seek

But the Lord God called to the man,
"Where are you?"
Genesis 3:9 (NIV)

We've all played hide and seek. It is a fun game when you are little. Whether it be in the closet or under the bed, you took great joy in trying to outsmart your opponent, hoping that they will eventually give up, resulting in you being crowned Best Hider. That doesn't work with God. There is no hiding from Him. There has never been a day that God has missed something you did.

And there is no creature hidden from His sight, but all things are naked and open to the eyes of Him to whom we must give account.
Hebrews 4:13 (NKJV)

You can't outsmart Him. He knows where you are at all times. He sees what's inside of you and what you've hidden from everyone else. It is exhausting to have to make up excuses or change the subject with God in order to avoid dealing with the real issues. While you are consumed with surface-dwelling, God is consumed with the deep wells inside of you that have been polluted by an unwillingness to "go there." What area(s) have you locked down so nothing or no one can get in? What are your designated "no-fly" zones? The problem with locking them down is that you can't get out either! In your attempt to protect yourself, you are actually losing yourself. Boundaries are one thing, but blocking life from getting into the areas where you have been burned can be detrimental to your health. Instead of looking at life through the scope of hope and optimism, you end up looking at life through the lens of bitterness and offense. Bitterness and offense can keep you behind bars, delaying your path to freedom. While you are stuck licking old wounds, the joys of life fade into the background, resulting in impotence. I've learned over the years not to close off any area of my life to God, as He has the ability to pry open any locked door and gain access to me by backing me into a corner, demanding that I give up the key. Submitting to the process was the key to my freedom and ultimately released me from the tension of the struggle. What does God have His finger on in your life? Are you trying to resist Him? It is futile to ignore or resist Him as He bears down on that area. If He wants it, give it to Him. It is for your good. Isn't that what you really want, though? Someone who has the ability to force you out of hiding and override your senses when you are acting crazy? To save you from *you*? Doesn't it give you a sense of relief to know that *Someone* already knows you, has seen your best and worst days but still wants a relationship with you?

Then the man and his wife heard the sound of the Lord God as he was walking in the garden in the cool of the day, and they hid from the Lord God among the trees of the garden.

Genesis 3:8 (NIV)

Adam and Eve hid (to withdraw, hide). (Bible Hub, n.d.) They tried to cover up what was already exposed to

God. This is what shame does. It causes us to withdraw into the shadows away from the very One who already knows the condition of our hearts. It brings with it a false sense of security that we are better off hiding than coming clean. Concealing the real you doesn't dissuade God from seeing the real you. Adam and Eve were already naked. Naked in body and naked in their emotions. God was okay with naked. He created them naked. Are you trying to hide something from God that He already sees? More specifically, running "to" or "among" something, thinking that somehow it will camouflage you? Notice that in verse 9 God was seeking them out. They were not seeking God. God's intent was to have an open relationship with them. He is always in pursuit of us in spite of our best attempts to avoid Him. He already sees our struggle. That's why He came. He is acquainted with our struggle.

For we do not have a high priest who is unable to empathize with our weaknesses, but we have one who has been tempted in every way, just as we are—yet he did not sin.

Hebrews 4:15 (NIV)

No amount of makeup or gender reassignment can hide it. While we try and hide it, God calls out to us so we can expose it to Him. This is what real love does. It confronts the sin that so easily entangles us and demands it be dealt with. The weight of sin is too much for you to bear. You were not designed to carry its weight. He will flash the scenes of our life across our faces so we can identify the places that reassigned our true identity to the fake ones that many are posing under today. The one we show to the world but not to God. The one that gives us access to the social circles of life but not intimacy with God. Underneath the pretense, He sees the fear that holds you in check, driving you into self-loathing and forfeiting the forgiveness that He readily has made available to you. His heart is to heal you so you can live. He is not interested in shoving you back in a box so you can hide. We are not perfect. God knows we are not perfect. We are born into a world that is not perfect. Adam and Eve's rebellion against God's rule thrust us into a downward spiral of sin (separation from God) that cannot be remedied apart from a relationship with Jesus Christ. We are born with a sinful nature with a desire to rebel.

Romans 3:10–12 (NLT) says,

"No one is righteous-not even one. No one is truly wise; no one is seeking God. All have turned away; all have become useless. No one does good, not a single one."

Your goodness does not carry weight when God looks at your spiritual condition. He knows we have fallen and cannot escape the penalty of that fall without His saving grace. Adam and Eve's disobedience landed them in the bushes, trying to hide what God already saw. What are you hiding?

Toby

I asked a friend of ours to share her story. The following is how she sees it...

I don't know if it was a southern thing or just a family of origin thing, but the first correction that ever stuck with me was *shame*. "Tobylee, you ought to be ashamed of yourself. You know better than to ." (fill in the blank to whatever the wrong-doing was.) I remember thinking, *Am I bad? Does this mean I am not worthy of being loved?* I remember spending the rest of that afternoon doing whatever I could to make up for what I did and earn that love, favor, and sense of belonging back. "Shame on you. That was rude. Unladylike. Ugly." "Such a shame to hear she got pregnant out of wedlock." "What a shame she must be to her family." And the list goes on! And that shadow followed me in everything I did.

Let's compound this shame with the following.

Age eight—molested twice by a close family friend. I stayed silent for fear of ruining the family's friendship and lived-in fear of this person. I never spoke of it until I was twenty-eight and then was blamed for being inside a home when the parents were gone. Now at the age of fifty-four, I am finally processing all the emotions of that day via counseling.

Age eleven—parents divorced. I had to choose which parent to live with in a court in front of both of them.

Age fourteen—pregnant out of wedlock when it wasn't

accepted like it is today.

My parents remarried a year after their divorce. I was twelve. It resembled a yo-yo at best, going back and forth for several years. My dad would ask my mom to come back home, only to have her leave three-six months later when their fights and anger could not be resolved. This went on for many years until I married and moved out at eighteen. I have been married four times.

Age nineteen—first divorce. Age twenty-four—second divorce. Age thirty-six—third divorce. Sprinkle sexual immorality in as well during the single months. At age thirty-eight, I was married to my fourth and current husband. This marriage, by far, has been the hardest emotionally.

All through life, I have struggled with low self-esteem, not being good enough, and all those thoughts, words, and behaviors that come along with having a tainted view of myself. My daily mantra was, "Are they mad at me? Do they like me? Did I do something to make them mad? How can I make them like me?"

In my home of origin, the motto was, "Do as I say, not as I do." Living and making decisions by emotions were exemplified in my home. No wonder when I didn't like something anymore—thought it too difficult—I just quit, walked away, or found something or someone new.

After my parents divorced, but before I got pregnant, I was on the road to a way of life of pleasing men for favors. I was twelve, looking like I was sixteen, being dragged to "family style" country bars by my eighteen-year-old sister. I learned quickly that with just enough make-up and my sister's clothes—tight and short—I could pretty much get what I wanted. I started drinking at the age of twelve. I hated how it tasted but liked the effect; I wasn't so fearful all the time anymore. I felt good. I felt pretty. I felt like I belonged. And so, this is how my life went for a few short years. I was the center of attention amongst my sister's older friends, and I loved it!

At age fourteen, I started dating a guy in high school and got pregnant. After four months of hiding it, I finally told my mom…she actually guessed it. It was a tumultuous confrontation, but we got through it, albeit more shame and blame were added to my already growing inventory during that encounter.

Getting pregnant and not being married was considered a sin and something to be ashamed of. However, I met Jesus in a real and personal way and had peace all throughout my pregnancy. I was not aware that this was called *salvation.* I just knew I felt His presence daily. I sensed that He allowed the pregnancy in order to save me. It saved me from a life on the streets. I was not fearful of the future or how I would raise the baby. I knew—completely trusted with blind faith—that He would provide for her. However, I was not as trusting if I would ever be loved or valued by another man in the future. After my daughter, Casey, was born, I was not involved in a Christian church, so I quickly turned back to the dating scene and sexual immorality. Somewhere along the way, I convinced myself of the lie that sex equated to love. And I lived out that lie. The one good thing that emerged from being a teenage mom was that I remembered the Lord instilling peace in me for this situation, allowing me to bear it. I knew I didn't have a choice but to do the best I knew how. The hardest part was being accepted by my peers. It was not as accepted back in the early '80s, and several of my friends were no longer able to hang around with me.

During my third marriage, and through Al-Anon twelve-step meetings, I met the Lord (again) and dedicated my life to Him. I willingly acknowledged Him as my Savior. I was twenty-seven years old. I was surrounded by strong women of faith, and my first Bible study was a deliverance ministry—as in real deliverance, seeing and witnessing people being delivered from every demonic thing imaginable. Not poltergeist demonic, but the real thing! I was raised Catholic. That kind of thing was never discussed. Yet, it intrigued me and scared me all at once. I was hooked. It was like spiritual psychology, and it made sense to me.

During this time, I felt the Lord start exposing areas of sin in my life. The old tapes from my childhood kept penetrating my thoughts. More shame and being shrouded in shame and not knowing it was a lie from the enemy. I struggled in the early years with my faith and trust in God. Did He really have my back? Will God really do it for me?

My third marriage was drowning in active alcoholism

(his) and codependency (mine). We were the poster children for dysfunction. By this time, I was actively walking with the Lord, but nothing was changing in my marriage. For twelve long years, I prayed for the Lord to save, heal, and deliver us. Mostly deliver him from alcoholism. Unfortunately, that did not happen, and I divorced him after his third affair. Not only did this further compound the shame shadow, but now we have God in the mix of not answering my prayers! Now the hook is in. He is capable for others but won't for me! I must be undeserving, unworthy, not favored, or valued enough! The victim mentality was birthed, and I turned away from everything and everyone spiritual. Divorced and living in Florida, supporting myself, I am now on my own road, making my own rules and seeking my own comforts.

Jump ahead five years, and I am now married again to my current husband with most of the baggage from all the above. The same feelings of low self-worth and definitely the shadow of shame are still very prominent in my life. I love the Lord, and I am doing my best to walk with Him, but still struggling with my trust. Looking back, I had not yet completely surrendered all my life because, well, I liked what I liked and wasn't quite ready to give it all up.

And then I signed up for C3 Fit Camp. The very thing I hate and all that it represents: discipline, hard work, commitment, physical pain and discomfort as well as failure, embarrassment and humiliation, and not being good enough or strong enough. In one word— *fear*. The same fear and dread I felt when I was eight-twelve years old came rushing back. I would be in a gym where all my weaknesses and vulnerabilities are exposed. There would be no more hiding.

A mutual friend of ours had been encouraging Som (current husband) and me to join him in getting healthy. We complained of being overweight but did nothing about it. He texted us both and challenged us to meet him for a spin class in a local gym. I took the bait. I started the spin class, and after a few months and 15lbs down, I felt brave enough to join his CrossFit gym. I was very intimidated by CrossFit, but while perusing the website, I saw that there was another type of workout. It was called C3 Boot Camp. I was not sure what that was, but after I read the description, I thought to myself, *I will sign up for that. How hard can that be?*

Oh, my dear Lord Jesus! How many times have I had to eat those words of "how hard can that be?" Can you say impossible!

Day One. I met Misty Sarlo, one of the owners of C3. She was so sweet and welcoming. She asked me how I felt, and I can remember that I was so scared that I just started crying. I literally felt sick to my stomach and wanted to turn around and run away. Little did I know that crying would be the theme of my workouts. Everything in that gym intimidated me. Everything!

As for day one's workout, she asked me to row and then did some kind of heel touch ab workout. *Not so bad,* I thought to myself. *I will come back.*

Day Two. I met Richie Sarlo, the other owner of C3 (little did I know how mightily God would use him). He was and is very knowledgeable. He wasn't too talkative and seemed pretty serious. I found it hard to read him, and that made me nervous. After about five minutes into the warm-up, he told me I was done as in *see you next time*. I was spent! I could not breathe, partly because I have asthma, and could not do more than three squats or hold a plank for more than three seconds! I was so humiliated. The shame that clouded me all through my childhood and young adulthood was back in full force. I bawled all the way home, made promises to myself that I was quitting and would *never* go back. I was pissed off! I also decided that day I didn't like Richie. *Who does he think he is?* (Oh, just wait. God hasn't quite shown off yet) On that drive home, I realized something bigger than me was going on. I felt a "pull" to go back.

Day Three. Richie again. Same as above. I could not complete the warm-up. And on this day, I met the Ring Row. I could only do one. Only *one*! I could not pull myself up after the second attempt. And out of nowhere, I started bawling my eyes out. At that moment, I felt stupid and weak, so filled with shame that I couldn't do something as simple as pull myself up (*that's probably a sermon*). And then, as usual, I was done for that day too. But before I was dismissed, Richie asked me why I was crying, and all I could think in my head was…*I used to do gymnastics. I used to swim, and just a few years ago, I was playing adult softball.* In my mind, I was still that person, but in reality, I was not! I had let myself go, got lazy, gained weight, and stopped caring. I don't remember what I responded with, but I knew it wasn't what had been all that I had been thinking. But I think he knew that I was done for the day! My fear, shame, and a boatload of pride kept my mouth shut that day.

At some point in the first or second week of being sent home after ten minutes of a fifty-minute workout program, I asked Richie—not so nicely—if I should just quit and go back to a regular gym until I was "strong enough" to do their workouts *(as if I would go and then come back, HA*)! I remember him giving me this strange look and saying he would have Misty call me. When she called, we talked about the struggle I was having, and I asked her the same question. She called me out in such a gentle manner. She said, "*No*! Do not leave; we will help you. You know you won't go to a gym and come back. So please stay with us, and I will modify your workout. Don't give up!" I knew her words were meant to encourage me, but they were not what I wanted to hear. (Looking back, I think God was laughing at the setup).

I decided to stay and see where this would take me. It was still humiliating to see my "special" workout written out on a board for all to see, but it kept me going, and I kept working and stuck it out. Every day was a mental battle with my baby workouts while watching and working with others who were so much stronger and, in my opinion, a lot more confident as they did the full workout. I just kept telling myself that one day, maybe, I would be able to do it. *One day I will be like they are.* But I had a long way to go!

Three times a week, I came to a hot warehouse with no AC, struggling to breathe due to asthma, smoking, and drinking on the weekends, which, by the way, Richie also knew and called me out on, especially with the smoking! He walked by me one day and just said, "The cigarettes aren't helping." I just busted out laughing and added that habit to the list to break. By this time, I had a healthy respect for him. I did my best to complete the workouts for the day as I cried, cussed, and silently told myself I was never coming back. Richie became my regular trainer. He saw me in my rawest form: hurting, struggling, crying, cussing, embarrassed, and full of pride, but he never said a mean or degrading word. Every now and then, I would just look up, and he would give a slight smile or a nod of encouragement. Somehow I knew he knew I had internal struggles going on but didn't understand how he knew. When I was feeling a bit more comfortable around Richie, I said to him, "I don't know where you are with your beliefs, but me working out is like a baby Christian reading the book of Revelation the day after they get saved." He did not respond with any words. He had no comment whatsoever but just smiled a genuine smile. I still had no clue.

About six weeks later, Misty was at one of our afternoon workouts, and she and I were talking. She invited me to her church. I had been praying for a home church and thought, *Wow, what a coincidence.* I asked her, "What church do you go to?" She said, "The Community Chapel in St. Pete." We talked a bit more, and I must have asked her about this church because she said, "It's our church, and we are about a year old now. *Richie is the pastor.*" I wished I could have seen the look on my face because I certainly thought, *Just kill me now! Lord, you can just open up the floor and swallow me whole!* I remember thinking, *I need to clean my mouth up!* Little did I know, that isn't all that was getting cleaned up. God knew exactly what I needed and who I needed, and He set me up. This has just now turned into a divine appointment!

I went to the Community Chapel in the summer of 2018 and knew I was home the first day. Jesus rekindled my love for Him and continued His work in my heart, mind, and soul. For the first time in my Christian walk, I asked Him to be my Lord. I felt his presence the same as I had when I was pregnant. I knew something was happening. I had a lot to walk through yet, but I knew I was going to have to walk through it.

Time goes on, and I am now about a year with C3; I have graduated from the modified modifications. I can now complete a warm-up and move on to my "baby workouts." On one particularly extremely grueling workout and hot day, I hit a wall. Out of nowhere, dread, fear, anxiety, and a feeling of being trapped and not being able to breathe came over me. It came over me so much I could not breathe and started hyperventilating. I thought it was asthma-related. Richie yelled out five more of whatever we were doing. I literally thought I was dying, but I pushed through it. I finished the fifth and ran outside. I needed air! I could not stand one more second in that hot warehouse. I felt trapped, and I panicked. I made it outside. I squatted down and knew instinctively this was not an asthma attack. I was not praying per se, but I can remember asking myself, "What is this? What is going on?" Right then, the Lord flashed the person who molested me across my face. I thought, *Now, Lord, we're going to do this now?* I am hot. I am hating life right now, sweaty, and I cannot catch my breath. You want to bring this up now! *Why?!* I felt like He said, "Yes, you need to deal with this and forgive him." I gathered myself, went back inside, and joined the others in whatever exercise they were on. I said a quick prayer about releasing this person to God and being willing to forgive him. Richie asked if I was okay. I said, "Yeah, just some childhood stuff coming up." He immediately poured out words of encouragement and praise. He was proud of me for not packing up and leaving. That day I felt whole-er. I felt strong. I felt good about myself. I did not tell him what it was that day, but I did share later what it had been about. I felt the love and compassion immediately from my pastor and knew God sent me to Richie and Misty on purpose.

The shame shadow has now been exposed to the light. That is the day I became aware that this was much bigger than just getting physically healthy. The process was already in the works, but that day is when I became aware of the bigger picture. That day the *Lord* made it perfectly clear He would use the very thing I hated most for my deliverance from all my shadows and their strongholds. I am still in the process. Many times, I have talked about being molested, but it was said as a matter of fact of something that happened to me. It is only just recently, with counseling, that I am actually processing and feeling the emotions of that day. It is hard, and there are times I want to "modify" those feelings and quit. But I am learning to stand still and allow the Lord to do what He is going to do because now I know I can do the hard things!

Go Dark

Growing up, we were conditioned to be afraid of the dark. We were told stories of the boogie man and monsters that would jump out of the closet. As kids, I can remember having a night light on so we could see. That light gave us some solace because it kept the "boogie man" at bay. Eventually, we got over being afraid of the dark—at least most people have—as we got older and realized that most of what we believed was due to childish thinking and immaturity. When you look at the origin of life, you see that life actually began in darkness:

In the beginning, God created the heavens and the earth. The earth was formless and empty, and darkness covered the deep waters. And the Spirit of God was hovering over the surface of the waters. Then God said, "Let there be light," and there was light.

Genesis 1:1–3 (NLT)

Darkness was the canvas that God started to draw on

when He created the world. God did and does some of His best work when it is dark. Photographers use a darkroom when they go to process photographic film and make prints. It is a room that can be made completely dark to allow the processing of light-sensitive photographic materials, including film and photographic paper. It is essential for the development of the pictures. In other words, pictures come to life when they are in a dark place. They are seen differently when in the dark. There's something about being in the dark that brings out the best in us. We have to pay more attention to where we are going, and our cognitive abilities are in a heightened state of awareness. Have you learned to embrace the dark areas of your life where it is hard to see? Has life shrouded your view, making it difficult for you to navigate? If we are not careful, we can look at the dark seasons of our life with contempt and bitterness, missing out on the opportunities for growth. No matter how dark it is, there is always a ray of light peeking through in even the most difficult of places. Look back over your life. Your journey has been filled with highs and lows, each etching a mark on you that shaped who you are today. Your identity has been forged in the embers of past experiences, both positive and negative. Those dark nights helped create in you a hunger for God. Because of our nature, we tend to remember disappointment and failure more than we do our victories. They seem to carry more weight. My aim is for you to shift your weight from disappointment and failure to the triumphs of your life. I played baseball growing up. I loved it. One of the things the coaches taught you when you were in the batter's box was to step toward the pitcher when the ball was coming at you when you were about to swing. Why? You would have a better chance of connecting with the pitch. We sometimes would get into a bad habit and step to the side or "in the bucket," as the coaches would call it, causing us to pull away from the pitch and minimizing our chances to connect. What am I saying? When we weren't in the right stance or "in the bucket," it was hard for us to generate the power we needed to connect with what was being thrown at us. In comparison, when you open yourself up to the lies of the enemy, you lose your ability to generate enough power to connect to the truth about who you are today. A lack of self-awareness can leave you searching for answers as to who you are, casting a shadow over your life, making it hard for you to play free. Recognizing its effects can help you make the necessary adjustments to help you step into who you were meant to be.

Brace for Impact

A couple of years back, I got my wisdom teeth taken out. If you have gotten your wisdom teeth taken out, you know what a "fun" experience this is. You get to be on the receiving end of the dentist taking out his frustration on you as he breaks apart your teeth. All kidding aside, I was prepped by more needles in my gums than I can remember. After I couldn't feel my cheeks anymore, the long, arduous journey of three extractions began. Yes, he left one in! The dentist started to dig around my wisdom teeth to soften the area for the demolition to begin. Keep in mind, I was awake and could feel what he was doing but couldn't see what he was doing. I was engaged in the process (it was hard not to as my face was contorting to levels that I didn't know it could contort to) and anxious to get this procedure done. After softening up the surrounding gums, he applied a massive amount of pressure on my wisdom teeth to start to break them up. After a few minutes of twisting my teeth back and forth, they began to break apart. One of my teeth made a b-line for the back of my throat, but my gag reflex kicked it back to the front of my mouth, where I caught it and proudly spat it out and kept on bracing for the next break. It was quite a scene: my dentist with one knee on his chair, his assistant, and my blood and other parts being sucked through what I call the mouth vacuum. This, coupled with the thoughts of "*Have you gotten them yet?*" were all working together to make this a memorable experience. Finally, my dentist got the last tooth out, but we weren't finished. The roots were left. This was the easy part, as what was in their way had been removed!

As I began to reflect on this process, it reminded me of God's process. When He is about to extract dead roots that have been decaying inside of us, He allows life to soften up the hard areas of our hearts. He then applies pressure to the wounded areas so they can begin to break again. Yes, God will re-break an area of your life so He can begin to heal it correctly. Little by little, He goes to work with the end goal of getting to the roots of what is infecting us, pulling and tugging on the infected areas until there ready to be removed. This is a painful and intimate process. A process between you and God that requires your undivided attention. He knows that surgery must be done for you to finally feel free and realize the relief of being loosed from the effects of those roots. Some of you are suffering from emotional halitosis. The stench of festering emotional trauma has corroded your ability to cope. You are in need of an extraction as those experiences have overridden your ability to receive the unconditional love of God. If you allow Him, the surgical hands of God will go to work on those wounds that are sabotaging your ability to receive that unconditional love. Inconsistent emotions, abandonment issues, and relationship miscues all play a role in your ability to receive that love. If we were given an inside view of the current condition of the hearts of those around us, we would see the entanglement of trauma that has rooted itself deeply into their lives. They are playing with clotted emotions that have slowed their pace. Bitterness has become a close friend and rejection—a close ally, repelling anything that is actually good for them. Rather than face the truth about what they are becoming, they turn to whatever medicates the problem. Sober judgment is far from their radar, and they have settled for the temporary relief of inebriation. The problem with inebriation is that it wears off, and like a crack addict looking for their next fix, you become obsessed with the next score. It could be sex. It could be validation—something that will alleviate the pain inside. Is this you? Or maybe someone you know? Numbing the real issues that need to be dealt with. Outwardly, posing as happy, but inwardly you are shrinking. You know you're not right, but you don't have the courage to face the truth about what you are becoming. Instead of doing the work to get better, you turn toward whatever is easy and familiar. You're not really living. You're just hiding, barricading yourself, using your bitterness and resentment as windows to the world you have created.

But the LORD God called to the man,
"Where are you?"
Genesis 3:9 (NIV)

It's not that God didn't know where they were. He wanted them to see how far they had drifted. Do you know where you are? Have you drifted from a place of intimacy with God? If you can hear Him still calling out to you, answer Him. He still wants a relationship with you. We have all blown it, and we still do. That doesn't disqualify you from being forgiven and beginning again. There might be some hurdles you have to overcome, but it doesn't mean you can't jump over them. The way back may be filled with uncertainty and difficulty, but that doesn't mean it's not worth it. You can be redeemed. God can redeem your time and help you make the most of the life that He has given you. It will, however, require your willingness to go under the knife and allow God to cut away the old fragments of your past and rebuild the broken places of your life. If you can still hear me through the pages of this book, you are more than your past failures and mistakes. If you turn your hurts over to God, you'll see that there is still a hope and a future for you.

RISE

When he came to his senses, he said, "How many of my father's hired servants have food to spare, and here I am starving to death!"

Luke 15:17 (NIV)

The story of the *prodigal son* reminds us of the weakness of human nature and the redemption of a heavenly Father. We are thrust into the story where the younger son of two wants his inheritance. The Father gives him what would be his, and the son leaves for a distant country. While there, he squanders his inheritance and ends up working in a pigpen. He is not unlike a lot of us who have known the protection of a Father but decide that leaving that protection for what we consider "greener grass would be better," only to find out that grass has brown spots wherever you go. You are not without options in life. You are not without temptation in life. The opportunity to fail exists. It is what makes life glorious but also terrifying at times. The possibility of failure is a deterrent for some people and steers them away from risk. What if you fail? Then you learn something in the process that will help you make a better decision tomorrow. Until you can define failure, then it will always be something that you dub as final. Failure is not final. What if you succeed? The tension between the both is what makes faith a necessity. It bridges the gap between fear and courage and allows me to step out knowing that there is *Someone* who already knows the outcome. He has provided saving grace for your learning curves even when you fall short. It's what makes following Christ an adventure. He knows the end from the beginning and is making all things new. Even in your mistakes, He is working it out for your good (see Romans 8:28). Freedom is not free. It has never been. It costs you. It opens you up to a world of possibilities that involve risk and reward. Given too soon, it can be detrimental to the health of an individual both spiritually, emotionally, and even financially. There is a reason why we have age limits on driving and drinking. Freedom without boundaries is costly. It can cause you to cast off restraint and expose yourself to a world that you are not ready for. We live in a world that is obsessed with making us grow up faster than we need to, making promises it can never deliver on. Promiscuity, drunkenness, and unhealthy behaviors make a bid for affections at a young age. We are bombarded with images that poke at our curiosity, awakening desires in us that should lay dormant until the right time. How many of you are still dealing with images that you saw when you were a kid? Don't get me wrong. I love adulting, but pushing an agenda that emphasizes loose women, mo' money, fast cars, and partying is narrow-minded and short-sided. I never understood the fascination with being drunk. I can count on my one hand the number of times I have been buzzed. I never felt the need to push the limits to see how smashed I could get. It always felt childish to me that someone would want to lose control of themselves, forget who they are, and wake up wondering what happened last night. Meeting the toilet for a ritual cleansing of my palette never was incentive enough to see how far I could get wasted. Why would you want to lose that much control and put your life in the hands of someone else because you can't see or talk straight? It's not attractive for a forty-five-year-old to slur his speech as he struggles to tell you how much he loves you. Or be hit on by a man twice your age because he has lost his inhibitions and has decided to go for it. If you need liquid courage to give you courage, you are not courageous. You are still a child who has used your freedom to hide who you really are. Why not do the work to become stable and find the courage that only comes from knowing your true worth?

David writes in **Psalm 16:5-6 (NIV)**,

Lord, you alone are my portion and my cup;
you make my lot secure.
The boundary lines have fallen for me in pleasant places;
surely I have a delightful inheritance.

The Lord wants you to enjoy life. He has set certain boundaries in place for your benefit and your protection. Over-riding the boundaries doesn't come without a cost. You are going to have to learn to live within the boundaries that have been set if you are going to experience the goodness of God while you are here on this earth. On the flip side, God is not going to take away the temptation to step outside of the boundaries either. He did not take away the temptation in the garden when He told Adam and Eve that they could eat of any tree except the Tree of Knowledge of Good and Evil (see Genesis 2:16–17). You have a choice in how you respond to temptation when it comes. The temptations that we face are common to man, and He will provide a way of escape so you can endure them (see 1 Corinthians 10:13). Contrary to popular opinion, God is not interested in killing your fun. He understands our need for fulfillment and satisfaction. However, you are limited in what you can do and where you can go. You are not built to live without restraint. You are built to carry unnecessary weight. Yet, I wonder how much unnecessary weight people are carrying just by living outside of their grace space. Should you be doing what you're doing? Are the expectations of others putting more weight on what you were designed to carry, driving a wedge between your true self and who everybody wants you to be? The grace that God has given them to walk in is not the same grace God has given you to walk in. Your job is to move with the grace of God in your life. You do a disservice to yourself by trying to "fill someone else's shoes." No matter how much you try to walk like them or talk like them, you will never be them. You were cut to size with a specific purpose and role to fill. Until you can connect with how you are hard wired, you will never disengage from the environments or relationships that don't fit your specifications. I am never going to play professional basketball. I am blessed with average height and a decent jump shot, but I am not wired to play professionally. No matter how much I might want to, my skill set doesn't lend me to play at the level. At some point, reality sets in, and you are going to have to accept the *grace* for the season that you are in and work with the skillset that you have been given. Letting go of what used to work is a monumental step in your growth process. My wife makes fun of me when I outgrow T-shirts. She says they look like baby tees on me. She is right. To continue to wear them would signify a lack of self-awareness. What worked for a time doesn't work anymore. With new seasons come new opportunities to expand the wardrobe of grace that God has blessed me with. Some of you have outgrown what you are "wearing" in life. I'm not talking about clothes but stigmas about your childhood and young adulthood that used to define you but don't anymore. Inside, you have changed. What you used to think was funny is not funny anymore. You know you have outgrown your friendship circles but fear being alone if you break away. Those clothes don't fit you anymore. God has promoted you. You've gone up a size in the way you think, process, and react to life. No matter how hard you try, you're just not going to get any smaller in the way you think.

Ralph Waldo Emerson said,

"The mind, once stretched by a new idea,
never returns to its original dimensions."

You were meant to keep evolving. To develop elasticity in the way you think, feel, and move. Don't apologize for growing. You don't need to shrink. You need to expand your wardrobe. Try out different styles of friend groups, schools of thought, and interests. Tap into the creativity that lies within you. Connect with what you love. Follow the scent of intrigue down the road to discovery. Some of you haven't even tapped into the best part of you yet. Keep tapping. This is what makes grace so amazing. It's transformational. It will permit you to change and illuminate the hidden version of yourself, bringing you into a fuller view. The prodigal son came to his senses and realized that better was waiting for him. How about you?

Rehab

...to be made new in the attitude of your minds;
and to put on the new self, created to be like God
in true righteousness and holiness.

Ephesians 4:23–24 (NIV)

If you watch sports on a regular basis, you will hear the commentators say, "Heat check." This refers to a player who is playing "out of his mind," hitting consecutive shots or scoring at will with varying degrees of difficulty. Often, you will hear a basketball player say, "I just needed to see one go in." Or you'll see a baseball player who is in a slump beat out an infield single. That single was all he needed to set him off on a hot streak. Something breaks when you start to see small wins. Often these small wins lead to bigger wins. We all get into slumps. That's what makes us human. The danger is in staying in those slumps. Left too long, we become fat with despair, and our minds darkened with the loss of hope. If we are going to become all that God has called us to be, there must be a shift in the way we think.

The Transtheoretical Model (also called the Stages of Change Model) was developed by James O. Prochaska of the University of Rhode Island and Carlo Di Clemente and several of their colleagues beginning in 1977. The model argues that individuals move through six stages of change: precontemplation, contemplation, preparation, action, maintenance, and termination.

Precontemplation. In this stage, people do not intend to take action in the foreseeable future (defined as within the next six months). People are often unaware that their behavior is problematic or produces negative consequences. People in this stage often underestimate the pros of changing behavior and place too much emphasis on the cons of changing behavior.

Contemplation. In this stage, people intend to start healthy behavior in the foreseeable future (defined as within the next six months). People recognize that their behavior may be problematic, and a more thoughtful and practical consideration of the pros and cons of changing the behavior takes place, with equal emphasis placed on both. Even with this recognition, people may still feel ambivalent toward changing their behavior.

Preparation (Determination). In this stage, people are ready to take action within the next thirty days. People start to take small steps toward behavior change, and they believe changing their behavior can lead to a healthier life.

Action. In this stage, people have recently changed their behavior (defined as within the last six months) and intend to keep moving forward with that behavior change. People may exhibit this by modifying their problem behavior or acquiring new healthy behaviors.

Maintenance. In this stage, people have sustained their behavior change for a while (defined as more than six months) and intend to maintain the behavior change going forward. People in this stage work to prevent relapse to earlier stages.

Termination. In this stage, people have no desire to return to their unhealthy behaviors and are sure they will not relapse. Since this is rarely reached, and people tend to stay in the maintenance stage, this stage is often not considered in health promotion programs.

—Wayne W. LaMorte
Doctor of Medicine and Master of Public Health
Boston University School of Public Health

If you talk to most people, they realize that some sort of change is necessary for them to achieve their goals.

It's a reason why so many gyms are packed with people motivated to begin every year starting in January. Sadly, that motivation wanes as New Year's resolutions turn into try again next year after only a short period of time. The drive for the better wanes as people are pulled away by other factors that become a priority in their life. I would also propose that the work required to change is also a barrier. It is difficult to change, especially when it involves doing something different. Rather than "work" at it, we look for cursory solutions that offer only short-term results. I get it. We are busy. However, I would argue that it has less to do with other factors and more with what we prioritize. Besides sickness or injury, there really is no excuse as to why physical and emotional health shouldn't be a priority in your life. In reality, sickness or injury should be motivating factors to get you on the road to better health! If everything we do flows from the wells that flow from within us, then doesn't it make sense to make sure those wells are stockpiled with the fuel that is needed to win at life? It matters what you put in you. It matters what you allow to influence your decision-making. Take your car, for example. It matters what fuel you put in your gas tank. If you put diesel fuel in a car that takes unleaded, the fuel pump will struggle to move the diesel through the system and clog up the fuel filter. Eventually, the diesel will move down into the engine, clogging up the fuel injectors and causing the engine to seize. Have you ever felt like you were walking through snow that is about waist-high? It's because something has clogged "your engine," making it difficult for you to walk. Life has a way of fogging our cognitive abilities. Over time, we get weighted down with incorrect thought processes that blur our line of sight, making it difficult to see where we are going.

Are you stuck? In need of a push? There is One who has the special equipment needed to get you out and get you moving again. However, it will require humility on your part and recognition of your need for Him. I would propose that there are many reading this book who are at this point. The gears of your life have ground down, and you are having a hard time shifting into the next gear. God is trying to get your attention. If jamming the circuit board of your life to get you to redirect your power source to Him is what it takes, then He will do it. This is what makes it so frustrating when it comes to our world. We run, abuse, and exercise our authority in unconscionable ways and think that God does not see. Is it a coincidence that we are now seeing the uncovering of plots and ethical immoralities on a regular basis? No. God is sick of it. When He is looking for something to change, He will expose it. What the enemy tries to hide, God reveals. He will expose what is hiding in the dark and bring it to light. He will uncover sin and put it on display. That's why imperative for you to heed His warnings, as eventually, the *truth* always takes center stage. It will reveal itself and tell the real story. We can't expect to do the same things continually and expect different results. It's the definition of insanity. The *why* behind what we do must be examined. How is it examined? It starts with your access point. Your conscience is that access point for God. He will ping that area of your mind to get you to think about why you are doing what you are doing.

As he journeyed he came near Damascus, and suddenly a light shone around him from heaven. Then he fell to the ground, and heard a voice saying to him, "Saul, Saul, why are you persecuting Me?" And he said, "Who are You, Lord?" Then the Lord said, "I am Jesus, whom you are persecuting. It is hard for you to kick against the goads."

Acts 9:3–5 (NKJV)

A goad is a farming tool fitted with an iron spike or point at one end, which was used to spur oxen as they pulled a plow or cart. It often had an iron scraper at the non-pointed end to clear clods of earth from the plowshare when it became weighed down. Sometimes the cattle would resist the driver resulting in them being poked. It was a reminder to keep moving forward. You are not in charge. Ultimately, the one driving the plow is. Saul finally came to that conclusion undoubtedly after many assaults to his conscience by the Lord. Saul was a zealot and intent on killing Christians and having them brought back to Jerusalem in chains (see Acts 9:1-2). It is futile to think that you can resist when God interrupts your current course of action. Eventually, your will and His will will collide, resulting in something breaking. And it won't be Him. Little did Paul know that this would be a defining moment in his life that would not only affect the trajectory of his life but of countless others to come. His *come-to-Jesus* meeting has changed the course of countless numbers of people as they look to his writings in the New Testament. I wonder what it will be for you. Are you in need of a course correction? Do you find yourself stuck in the middle of a hard-fought values fighting between your conscious and your actions? Are you working a job where the company's ethical obligations are less than ideal, and you are wondering if you should continue? Are you the problem? Are you engaging in a lifestyle that is contrary to how you grew up? Are you prioritizing pleasure over purpose? Do you look in the mirror and wonder, "Where has the time gone?" "How did I get here?" It is time for a *come-to-Jesus* meeting. Gone are the dreams that you once had. Life's intrusions have pushed you out of the way and forced you into hiding. Hiding behind false facades and a mask that keeps you protected from the sting of your life's choices. Your life is not what you dreamed it, and you keep looking for ways to fill up your glass that is always half empty. You don't tell anybody, but secretly you envy your friends and family members who are living their best life while you try to pick up the pieces of your own. I want you to fill in this phrase, "Life would be very different if..." Have enough courage to answer it, looking past the reality of today and the possibility of it never happening. Until you can voice it, the reality of the present will stiffen the possibility of the future. You must work toward thinking differently. What has worked its way into your life that won't allow you to think past where you are? Is it generational? Is it something that you picked up along the way? Let's be honest. Not everything we learned growing up was beneficial. If your family member was prone to wander and introduced you to porn, you might have a distorted view of relationships. If you were touched inappropriately by a family member or friend, your line of sight might be off a little when it comes to relationships. Haven't you stopped to wonder why you are the way you are today? Why do you lean in certain directions when it comes to love and pleasure? Why have you made it this far? It wasn't because you made all the right decisions or had the best opportunities. Despite all your wanderings and searches for significance, there was *Someone* looking out for you, protecting you, and leading you to this moment where a decision must be made. Will you continue down the road of heartache and misalignment, or will you seize the opportunity to make a change? Often, crisis becomes the clarion call for change. It forces you to cry out for answers that were unwilling to reveal themselves until that crisis rang your doorbell. It is the delivery system for breakthroughs, and creativity is given an opportunity to speak, sparking life change. You were not meant to stay trapped in your own idealism but released to the reality of something bigger. We *are* part of something bigger and to stay trapped in our own limited mindset is a slap in the face to the One in whose image we were created (see Genesis 1:26). You may not be able to see your way out right now, but you are seen. That understanding must become a revelation to you. It will give you the strength to keep pursuing the answers to life that go beyond your comprehension.

We can't stop the propulsion of life, but we can ride the

waves of change to our ultimate destination. If you can see yourself from the viewpoint of eternity, then what you experience here is minute compared to what lies ahead. If death is inevitable, doesn't it make sense to want to live? Why stay stuck sowing in fields that produces little to no results when you can engage in a purpose that goes beyond you? If the afterlife is the end game, then why not get plugged into the Source that is going to help you get there?

Ride or Die

We hear the phrase "Ride or Die" come up when referring to a friend who is with us no matter what. They have your back when others don't. They are willing to go with you to the end, or they *say* they will go with you to the end. In truth, you can count on one hand the people who really have your back when it counts the most. Jesus was not unfamiliar with ride-or-dies. He called twelve, had an inner circle of three, and many more who would follow Him because of the miracles He would perform. John 6 is filled with difficult teachings as Jesus turns up the heat on those who have been following Him for a while. Time does not permit me to go through the whole chapter. But I do want to draw your attention to verses 61–66 (NIV). Keep in mind that Jesus is fresh off His proclamation about eating His flesh and drinking His blood.

Aware that his disciples were grumbling about this, Jesus said to them, "Does this offend you? Then what if you see the Son of Man ascend to where he was before! The Spirit gives life; the flesh counts for nothing. The words I have spoken to you—they are full of the Spirit and life. Yet there are some of you who do not believe." For Jesus had known from the beginning which of them did not believe and who would betray him. He went on to say, "This is why I told you that no one can come to me unless the Father has enabled them." From this time many of his disciples turned back and no longer followed him.

I am not here to argue whether Jesus was preaching cannibalism or not. We are, however, given a front-row seat to the reality of the gospel message. It offends. It is not culturally or socially accepted by all. It separates. We are not given a demographic breakdown of those who were present during this dissertation, but we do know that many had been following Jesus until this moment. He challenged their belief system to get them to think differently. It was over their head, but I believe He wanted it there. Playtime was over. It was time to see who the true believers were. The ones who had the guts to keep believing when others have decided they can't go any further.

"You do not want to leave too, do you?" Jesus asked the Twelve. Simon Peter answered him, "Lord, to whom shall we go? You have the words of eternal life. We have come to believe and to know that you are the Holy One of God."

John 6:67–69 (NIV)

I am afraid that this question has been asked many

more times by Jesus to His followers, resulting in more turnover than retention. The gospel will weed you out. It is not for the faint of heart or the heartthrobs who are just looking for someone to rescue them or love them. It is for people who are willing to deny themselves and take up their cross and follow Him (see Luke 9:23). It is a denial of self and an invitation to exchange your life for the life Christ came to give you. It is a walk of faith. It is not a life of convenience. It is a yes to being offended and misunderstood and the unveiling of the supernatural. You have been given a lease on life, living on borrowed time with a timestamp when it will end. I want to talk to those who have taken a hard right away from Jesus. Life has hit you hard, and you have decided that walking away from Him is better than walking with Him. You may not understand everything that has happened to you, but are you willing to risk eternity for the temporary afflictions of life? Can it be that you have misinterpreted His purpose for your life? You are not alone. Even by those who call themselves Christians, accepting the word of God as inerrant and living a life that is pleasing to God is a struggle. Believing there is *Someone* who came and died for you and knows you is a hard pill to swallow when the lights go out, and you find yourself wondering if you are going to have enough to feed your family this week. Emotional gaps and nagging memories of past hurts can put a clamp on anything that is actually good for you. Losing loved ones brings to the light the fragility of life, causing you re-prioritize what matters most. The brevity of life should cause a sense of urgency to make the most of every opportunity you have been given. To make sure you do what you have been put on this earth to do. Sadly, this is not always the case. As loved ones depart, there are those who succumb to grief and never make it out. Having a chance to start over becomes too daunting of a task as memories of how it used to be run through their mind daily. They blame God for taking them too early, forgetting that their times are in His hands (see Psalm 31:15). Life is not over just because you got "hit" with something. Loss is part of life. You are not the only person to have your life interrupted by tragedy. Many have seen loved ones commit suicide or succumb to debilitating diseases. Others have lost loved ones in service to their country. Kids have witnessed their parents' divorce because of abuse and infidelity. You don't have a corner on the market when it comes to loss or tragedy. Have you been to an assisted living facility lately? I occasionally get to go in and connect with residents who are a shell of their former selves. It is a reminder to keep things in perspective. It is also a motivator! To do everything I can to stay independent physically and mentally. To sharpen the faculties that God has given me so I can fulfill my purpose. By God's grace, I'm going out with vigor and staying active until He decides to bring me home. How about you?

Win

It is always interesting to me when players and coaches get interviewed after a game. The range of emotions runs from elation to despair as they reflect on what they did or didn't do to affect the outcome. What you learn from these interviews is the importance of emotional well-being.

Emotional well-being is the ability to produce positive emotions, moods, thoughts, and feelings and adapt when confronted with adversity and stressful situations. (BetterUp.com, n.d.)

Your emotional well-being is most tested under pressure. In fact, it *shines* under the spotlight of adversity. Can you still produce when the odds are against you? *Rocky 2 (1979)* is one of my favorite Rocky movies in the Rocky collection. It stars Rocky (Sylvester Stallone) and Apollo Creed (Carl Weathers). Rocky is an upstart southpaw who faces off against Apollo Creed in a rematch for the championship belt. He is faced with the reality of facing the same boxer who narrowly defeated him in their previous fight (watch Rocky 1). He is outmatched and an underdog but has one thing going for him resolve. As the movie unfolds, he is faced with an unknown variable on his road to the rematch. Adrian (Talia Shire) is pregnant and ends up in the hospital, where she delivers her baby prematurely. They find out that she was hemorrhaging when she was brought in and, as a result, loses a lot of blood and slips into a coma. Rocky is supposed to be training for his rematch with Apollo Creed but is now faced with the reality of an uncertain future. With his wife bedridden, he is at her side and waits in anticipation for her to wake up. The movie turns on one word. As Adrian comes out of a coma and Rocky is introduced to his son for the first time, Rocky tries to get out of his fight with Apollo Creed, but Adrian retorts,

"There's one thing I want you to do for me. Win. Win!"

That push gave him the fuel that he needed to get back after it! He goes on to defeat Apollo Creed by one second in one of the most memorable last-round fight scenes in a movie of all time. Exhausted, with both eyes swollen shut because of the fight, he ends up on the ring floor with Apollo, both struggling to beat the ten count by the referee. Rocky wills himself to the ropes and ends up staggering to his feet as the referee counts ten before collapsing into the arms of one of his trainers. He wins! I realize that life doesn't always go the way of a Hollywood movie, and you're not always declared the winner, but there is something to be said about a person who laces up his shoes and shows tremendous resolve in the face of insurmountable odds. To push past the temptation to quit and reach down past the lingering feelings of doubt into the depths of possibility. You are capable of more than you think. You are stronger than you think. Your ability to push past temporary pain or discomfort qualifies you for promotion…Remember Jesus?

For the joy set before him, he endured the cross,
scorning its shame,
and sat down at the right hand of the throne of God.
Hebrews 12:2 (NIV)

His ability to take the temporary pain of the cross qualified Him to sit down next to His Father. In God's eyes, purpose trumps pain. He will allow you to experience it because He knows the growth that is waiting on the other side of it. It is also the gateway to freedom and purpose. How you handle it will either push you to become the person God intended you to be or cripple you. The fear of pain can also cause you to sidestep the very opportunities God has placed in your life for growth. You are going to grow. Grow older. Grow wiser. Delaying the inevitable doesn't abdicate its reality. Attempting to slow down the aging process doesn't make it go away. Trying to live in reverse doesn't work. We can't reverse what has already been done. You are moving toward your ultimate destination. I realize that it is necessary to "go back" in order to go forward at times but reliving your teen years in your 30s and 40s is a stretch. Your best days are ahead. Not behind you! Remember, your goal is your emotional well-being. The ability to respond well in the face of adversity. If you're always looking to go back to the way it was, you are missing the point of the cross. The cross changed everything. Jesus' death gave you a new starting point for real life. Not life like it was, but a rebirth into something new. A new life in Christ! Keep moving!

Go to Work

In the events that have preceded us, we saw a booming economy. People were working, and the unemployment rate was the lowest it has been in recent history. Derailed by the pandemic, we were forced to get creative. On the backside of the pandemic, companies started offering sign-on bonuses just to get people to start working again (and they still are). Companies you would have never thought of. In Pinellas County, Florida, Dunkin' Donuts was advertising a $500 sign-on bonus and weekly attendance bonuses. Target was offering up to $13 an hour. Healthcare companies were offering astronomical sign-on bonuses and salaries for traveling positions just to get people to start working. Companies are hiring, and we need to work. We live in a time where it is easier to get a handout than to go to work. Large unemployment checks and stimulus money has made it easier for people to stay at home. As a result, we have disincentivized people from going out and making a better life for themselves. I realize that every state is different, but it's time to go back to work. To press play and continue the legacy you were building two years ago before the pandemic hit. Yes, the world is a very different place, but we have to be careful that we don't stay in a perpetual state of receiving and never get back to producing. Do you want to be made well financially? Laziness is just as much of an issue as over-working can be. You might be saying, "I can't find work right now." Really? I live in the state of Florida. Gov. Ron Desantis has done a great job in keeping this state open and allowing the free market to bounce back. Businesses are hiring. The question is, "Do you want to work?" People have specifically moved to this state to work. Why? Because people want freedom and prosperity. No matter how much you try to control the narrative, most people will always see past jaded agendas. Eventually, motives are revealed, and the truth always comes out. No matter how much you try to dictate to people what they can or can't do, in the end, freedom always reins. At the core of who we are is an innate sense that we are called to something bigger than ourselves. Anything that infringes on that sense of calling results in an outcry. People get sick and tired of circling around the same wagons with no progress, and they will fight like hell to make sure they see brighter days ahead.

We talked about this earlier in the story of the man who was lying by the pool of Bethesda. Jesus is asking you the same question He asked him, "Do you want to be made well?" Then it might require taking a job that you may not love in order to get moving again. Movement. That's what we're after. Movement in your finances. Movement in your emotions. Movement in your mental health. If you work at home, make sure you are building in rhythms of movement and exercise. Sedentary lifestyles are a breeding ground for obesity and lack of motivation. If you don't like the way you look or feel, fix it. Take some steps toward a healthier lifestyle. It will result in a fresher flow of ideas and productivity. Will it be easy? No. Each day will bring with it new challenges mentally you will have to overcome. Keep climbing! Do something hard! It will challenge your comfortability and build up your self-efficacy.

Keep Digging

One of the movies that my kids loved to watch when they were younger was *Finding Nemo (2003)*. I have to admit I liked it too. Dory was one of our favorite fish.

She was absent-minded, caring, and loyal. She is helping Marlin find his son, Nemo. He is having one of those days, and she says to him,

"When life gets you down, do you know what you gotta do? Just keep swimming."

Simple but life-changing, right? The mental strength needed to make strides to improve the quality of your life is the key to your consistent success. God will interrupt your process. His interruptions are opportunities for course corrections and lifestyle changes. They are par for the course when it comes to a real relationship with Him. It is a matter of keeping your composure as you move through those interruptions. Not being perfect but making up your mind that nothing is going to stop you from achieving your gold. In the end, ultimately, God's purpose will prevail.

Many are the plans in a person's heart,
but it is the Lord's purpose that prevails.

Proverbs 19:21 (NIV)

We are inundated with self-help books on how to get better. In reality, there is only One that can help you get better. It's Jesus. Yes. The most controversial name in history. Wars have been fought over Him. Marriages have ended because of Him. Friendships have been lost because of Him. The sobering realization is that one day you will have to give an account for your life.

Nothing in all creation is hidden from God's sight.
Everything is uncovered and laid bare before the
eyes of him to whom we must give account.

Hebrews 4:13 (NIV)

How you live matters! What you desire matters. What you cast your affections toward says a lot about what you value. What does God value? You! Thanks to all the fans who used to hold up those *John 3:16* signs at sporting events (and Billy Graham), we know that…

For God so loved the world that he gave his one and only Son, that whoever believes in him shall not perish but have eternal life.

John 3:16 (NIV)

The issue is with the cross. How can a man claiming to be God willingly give up His life for a people that He created? Furthermore, give up His life for people who would ultimately reject His sacrifice? Why would He want a relationship with me? What does He really want from me? We must keep digging to find the answers. Digging is not an easy process but a necessary one if we are going to discover what lies beneath the surface. I had the privilege recently of helping a school with the renovation of the front and back of their property. They wanted to beautify the school in preparation for the new school year. Bags of mulch, shovels, paintbrushes and new plants were just some of the items that we used for this project. Teams were split up, each with a different focus for the day. One of the most time-consuming projects was turning a ground filled with hard shells into a beautiful flower bed. We had to remove the hard shells and clear out any underlying debris before we could lay down the mulch. We then dumped soil into the ground and dug around the edges, creating a bed for the flowers to grow. This process reminded me of how our life looks when we meet Jesus Christ. We are filled with debris left there by the hardness of some of the hits that we have taken by life. Without the right filtration system, that debris gets stuck in hard-to-reach places and ends up buried behind closed doors and missed opportunities. Over time the inner part of us (the most important part) erodes as the debris from those past experiences hardens our hearts and blocks the flow of life that Christ died to give us. Eventually, the memory of how we used to feel disappears into the cavern of self-deprivation. This results in emotional dehydration. The solution? We need a data dump. To empty the scripts from our pasts and childhood memories. To process the disappointments of battles we have lost so we can move on. If we can't reckon with the fact that we will never be good enough or strong enough to redeem our past, we will waste our lives trying to fix what Jesus can only fix. This is the problem that I have with cancel culture. Trying to erase the past by getting rid of history books and tearing down statues doesn't eradicate the fact that it happened. Trying to look the other way, cover your eyes, and pretend that something didn't happen causes spiritual cataracts (cloudiness) to develop. We can't escape the horrors of the past. You must face them if you are to be free and allow the healing balm of God to soothe the parts that have burned you. Some of you need to face yourselves. Look yourself in the mirror and make a determination that you will not succumb to the emotional noose that is tied around your neck. It's trying to suffocate you. The sobering truth is that life is too complex of a puzzle for you to solve on your own. It's complicated with many moving parts. Once you think you have whipped one part of your life, another one springs a leak. It's not that it wasn't there. It just hadn't been triggered yet! Triggers set you off and reveal wounds that have been concealed. God, in His attempt to help you deal with them, will force them to the surface so He can free you from their hold. That's why *forgiveness* is such a big deal to Him. He knows the power that you lose when you don't forgive. Forgiveness is a choice. Forgiveness is not predicated on whether someone else reciprocates it back to you. It is for you! God wants you to be free. No matter what has been done to you, God asks that you release the offense to Him. I know some of you might be thinking right now, "I can never forget what they did to me." I didn't say forget. Walking in forgiveness is a process. You may never forget the offense, but you can start to walk in freedom and feel the peace that only comes as you choose to forgive. Life is too short for you to miss out on all the goodness that God has planned for you to walk in. Stop letting some event or person control the way you live. They're running your life! Or maybe it's you. You're the control freak. Have you ever noticed that the more you try to manipulate or control, the less control you feel? We all have control issues to a certain extent but having to control someone or something because you feel out of control is a sign of immaturity. It leads to abuse and misuse of time, resources, and relationships. There are three principles that we try and put into practice in my house: *obsession, confession,* and *cessation.*

Obsession. We are obsessed with God and His purpose. We make it a priority to be about God's business. Whether it's at church, home, school, or places of influence, we realize that God has placed us there for a reason and a season.

Confession. We are not perfect, but we are in process. When an issue presents itself, we try and address it, so it doesn't come back to bite us later. We encourage self-reflection. To look in the mirror and call ourselves out on things we are seeing in ourselves. We endorse free speech and communication with each other as we process through adversity. We are all being realigned and realize that our cognitive abilities play a huge part in how fast we get to where God wants us to be physically, emotionally/mentally, spiritually, and financially.

Cessation. We aim to embrace endings and new beginnings as we let go of the old to embrace the new. This involves letting go of unrealistic expectations, relationships, and attitudes that are counterproductive to our growth, setting boundaries, and leaving the past behind.

Being uncomfortable with change is normal, but it is also necessary. Your desire for comfort will be the enemy of your progress. You can't afford to miss out on the beauty of life just because of the ashes along the way. The rubble of your life is where God breaks ground and changes your makeup to identify with the cross. The cross is the starting point for change. It was where Jesus declared that the old has gone and the new has begun. What will you do with its reality? You can't cancel it. The price has already been paid. You can't pretend that it never happened. History has proven otherwise. Whether it fits into your narrative of religion or makes you feel uncomfortable, it requires a response from you. All new roads lead through the cross. You will have to come to grips with its reality if you are going to see real change in your life.

Run

He isn't here! He is risen from the dead, just as he said would happen.
Come, see where his body was lying.
Matthew 28:6 (NLT)

As Christians, we celebrate the fact that the tomb is empty. He died and rose again. This is the cornerstone of our faith. No death or resurrection, and we are still stuck without the hope of redemption. With this being said, why are so many still living like His body is still in a tomb? Bound by fear and unbelief, they retreat into the tombs of doubt where there is no light or solace. It does not have to be this way! There is power in the cross and wonder-working power in the blood of Jesus to wash away the stain of sin and past regret. No matter how much you have done or what sins you have committed, Jesus has the power to forgive (see I John 1:9).

So, why are you still stuck? Is it because you think you have to pay unjustly for the wrongs you have committed? Or is that punishing yourself makes you feel better? Do you need to forgive yourself? We are not talking about not having consequences for your actions. There are always consequences, but keeping yourself in chains for a mishap that happened twenty-five years ago is foolish. Sadly, there are some that think that God overlooks sin and that somehow they can get away with abusing the grace of God. Look at our prisons; they are filled with people who are suffering consequences for their actions. God can and will forgive, but it doesn't mean there are no repercussions for our actions. It would make God unjust. Righteousness and justice are the foundation of God's throne (see Psalm 89:14). Look at your own life. Can you honestly say that you have not experienced ramifications for things you have done in your "former" life? Everyone has. It does not nullify God's goodness but illuminates His righteousness and justice and gives weight to the validity of who He says He is. God is going to watch over His word to perform it (see Jeremiah 1:12). He honors His word above His very Name (see Psalm 138:2, NKJV). That truth alone should help us steer away from the misuse of God's grace. So why did He come? His heart can be summed up in **Luke 4:18–19 (NLT)**:

"The Spirit of the LORD is upon me,
for he has anointed me to bring
Good News to the poor.
He has sent me to proclaim that captives
will be released,
that the blind will see,
that the oppressed will be set free,
and that the time of the LORD's favor has come."

The Poor: destitute, spiritually poor, either in a good sense (humble, devout persons) or bad. (Bible Hub, n.d.) In a world of fake news and made-up controversies, there is still *good news!* Jesus has come to set people free. I am old enough to remember when the movie *Forrest Gump* came out. Released in 1994, it featured Tom Hanks (Forrest Gump) as an optimistic individual who inspired people to believe that anything was possible. His witty sayings and heartfelt attitude about life and people captivated audiences. I can remember one scene from the movie that still impacts me today. As a boy, he is being bullied by a group of boys his own age. After getting hit with rocks, Jenny turns to him and says, "Run, Forrest, run!" As he started to walk and then run, the leg braces that had him grounded began to break off, catapulting him to a speed and distance he had never experienced before. The boys who had previously been chasing him on bikes stopped in frustration as he "dusted" them. Imagine the exhilaration he felt as what was weighing him down was no longer an issue, and he could feel the brisk clean air against his face and experience life in a way he had never experienced before. Could it be that whatever is holding you would break if you just started running? I'm not talking about physically running but running in the direction of truth. If Jesus came so I can be free, doesn't it make sense that anything that is attempting to bind me is not His will for me? So why are so many still bound? They are bound by their own inner lawyer as they struggle to put the pieces of their life together. They become their own judge and jury. Have you tried running with something around your ankles? It is virtually impossible as you can't put one foot in front of the other without feeling resistance or tripping. It's a reason why the author in Hebrews writes:

> *Therefore, since we are surrounded by such a huge crowd of witnesses to the life of faith, let us strip off every weight that slows us down, especially the sin that so easily trips us up. And let us run with endurance the race God has set before us.*
>
> **Hebrews 12:1 (NLT)**

What are you carrying that you shouldn't be? Is it an unrealistic expectation that you have set for yourself? A relationship that has become abusive, but you're too afraid to speak up? Emotional baggage? I don't like feeling trapped or bound, partly because it reminds me of what I used to feel like. Trapped in emotional deficits, I hid in relationships trying to overcome my inferiority and feelings of inadequacy. It wasn't until I fully gave my life over to Christ that I fully became aware of my need for a Savior and started to experience the freedom that Jesus said He came to give me.

Wrestle

In Genesis 32, we see the reunion of two brothers, Jacob and Esau. Separated by a birthright blessing gone bad (see Genesis 27), they are confronted with the opportunity to change. Jacob specifically is the focal point of the story. He is on his way to meet Esau. He had done all he could to try and pacify his bother before they met. He sent over…

200 female goats, 20 male goats, 200 ewes, 20 rams, female camels with their young, 40 cows, 10 bulls, 20 female donkeys, and 10 male donkeys.

Genesis 32:14–15 (NLT)

Jacob was a manipulator. His name means supplanter. He was acting in accordance with his nature, trying to manipulate his brother to avoid possible confrontation. He was doing what he had done his whole life, attempting to manipulate the outcome so that it ended in his favor. The real issue wasn't his brother but him. After sending his servants and livestock over to meet Esau, God enters the scene:

This left Jacob all alone in the camp, and a man came and wrestled with him until the dawn began to break. When the man saw that he would not win the match, he touched Jacob's hip and wrenched it out of its socket.

Genesis 32:24–25 (NLT)

This was not an ordinary wrestling match. This was a transformation on a deeper level. God was at work transforming who Jacob believed he was and who others had labeled him to be.

Then the man said, "Let me go, for the dawn is breaking!" But Jacob said, "I will not let you go unless you bless me." "What is your name?" the man asked. He replied, "Jacob." "Your name will no longer be Jacob," the man told him. "From now on you will be called Israel, because you have fought with God and with men and have won."

Genesis 32:26–28 (NLT)

God is big on identity. Jacob's name is changed to

Israel; God fights. When God is getting ready to bless you, He will break you in your most vulnerable place first. The place that is boarded up, separating you from the real you and *the you* that the world sees. The place that you fight from. Your deficit. The place that yields little to no fruit. It is what makes you ineffective as a person. It will cause you to wilt under the pressure of confrontation. It's the place you make your bed in when challenges come and the places you hide when you feel out of control. These deficits are your places of vulnerability and the breeding ground for your enemies to attack. God knows better than anybody what it's going to take for you to change. If you have not already, eventually, you will meet God in a wrestling match over your identity. God will choose the ring. The length of the fight is determined by God. Once the change has taken place and there has been an erosion of your former self, He will let up. Jacob goes from fighting God to clinging to God. God knows that your greatest need is Him. He is the only One who can transform your thinking, your attitude, and perspective. Too many people are misaligned and misinformed, thinking that they are something when they are not, exercising some form of godliness but not having real power. They have pledged allegiance to a progressive way of thinking that has water-downed their effectiveness. Their need to belong has given way to outside-the-box thinking that is neither progressive nor productive but dangerous and callous. **Genesis 1:27 (NLT)** tells us that we are image-bearers of God.

So God created human beings in his own image.

In the image of God he created them;
male and female he created them.

To tamper with that image causes self-destructive behavior that exalts idolatry and sets the stage for consequences you are not prepared to suffer. You can try and change the parts, but it does not negate the fact that God created mankind in His image. The understanding of this is crucial to your liberation and identity. Until you can identify with who God says you are, you will continually wrestle with thoughts of inadequacy. He will intrude on your interpretation of who you are to get you to see it His way. After walking with God for a while, you will see that His agenda takes priority over yours. His methods might be unconventional, the pain overwhelming at times, but the results are proven and everlasting. One way or another, you will learn what God is trying to teach you. He will get His message across to you. Jacob's limp was a reminder of God's ability to wound. Wound you for a purpose. Like a tattoo artist going to work on his craft, God will leave His marks on you to serve as a reminder that you are His. There are some marks that you don't talk about, but occasionally, when the situation presents itself, those scars flare up. Beneath the make-up and Instagram posts, there is much to our stories that we don't share. We cast the abbreviated, highlighted version to the world, but if we're honest, many of us are still suffering from what I call PTTD—post-traumatic trial disorder. You don't talk about it at parties or the club, but you can still feel the casings from previous battles clanging around in your head and in your heart. Those experiences have left an indelible mark on you. They serve as a reminder of a change point in your life. Jacob is presented with an opportunity to change. To finally admit who he was to his Creator and allow the Creator to change him. What a relief. An opportunity to finally stop running and discover who he really was. God did him a favor when He confronted him. How exhausted he must have been from living a duplicitous lifestyle. Some of you are exhausted from running. You are living a duplicitous lifestyle, showing dexterity at work or home but hiding emotional affairs and addictions. It's wearing on you. You're trying to keep it from coming out, but it is getting increasingly difficult to hide it. Even as I write this book, I can sense God getting ready to confront what needs to be exposed. Your secrets are killing you. You know it. God knows it. The threat of exposure is becoming too much to bear. I know you don't want to admit it, but secretly you wish it could be exposed. The pressure of living two different lives is too much to carry. Good news?! God loves you enough to confront you, so you don't have to! That's why you are feeling the pressure right now to get it right with Him. Are you terrified? Feeling anxious? Deprived? Out of control? Exhausted from running? It's time to wrestle.

Fly

According to statistics, whenever we fly, we have a one-hundred-thousandth of one percent (.000014%) chance of dying! To put this in perspective, you have a better chance of dying from a bee sting (1 in 5.5 million) than dying on a commercial flight (1 in 7 million). (Anxieties.com, n.d.)

I love flying. The sights, sounds, and even the smells of the airport. Except for my near-death experience mentioned earlier in this book, most of my experiences have been enjoyable. However, I remember when I first started flying, I was always nervous about the takeoff. The thought of soaring was a phenomenal feeling, but so was the fear of falling. I knew if I could just get up into the air, I would feel better. The struggle for me was to believe that the plane had enough power (and the pilot—enough skill) to get me where I needed to go. Through clenched teeth and white knuckles, I have learned to appreciate the power of being able to fly. Sadly, there are many who never take off in life because of ground control. They are controlled by their own fear of success and even failure. Failure is an option, but so is flying. If you can get over the fear of failure, the possibility of flying becomes more of a reality. Sometimes you just have to close your eyes, jump and see where you will land. I can remember watching the long jump in the 2021 Olympics. It was fascinating to see these athletes take flight and reach distances of over twenty-seven feet. You can't reach these distances if you are afraid to jump. They wouldn't be very effective at what they were doing if every time they started running, they were afraid of how far they would go and pulled up as they took off from the line. Perhaps your fear of failure is slowing you down as you run. I tell my fitness clients all the time that we are working to failure. If it doesn't hurt, it doesn't help. If there is not some level of discomfort, then we are failing to progress. It does us no good to lift what we can or pull what we can and then stop when it starts to tax us. You stop when you can't. If we are not pushing ourselves, we are cheating ourselves out of growth.

I have a friend who is a mental health counselor who tells her story like this…

My ex-husband used to have to drive over the Skyway Bridge (St. Petersburg, Florida) a few times a week for Sarasota service calls. One day he told me he was having anxiety attacks going over the bridge, and he needed help getting over it so he could do his job. I told him I would drive over it with him. So the next day, he and I and the kids started driving south to the bridge. When we got near it, he said, "I can't do it. You are going to have to drive until I get over this." I said, "Okay," and I did. After that, every time he had a service call, I would drive him and the kids back and forth across the bridge. Every time he would get anxious and breathe fast and shallow, I would say, "Eddie, it's okay. Look, it's beautiful up here." He would just say, "I can't do it, oh my gosh, it's so high. I can't stand it." This went on for some time until one day…I was driving us back to St. Petersburg, and on the approach to the bridge, he started saying, "Oh my gosh, how can you drive this? It's so scary. I can't even breathe!" Suddenly, I got scared too! I looked at the looming bridge ahead of me, pulled off on the right shoulder, and stopped the car. I looked at him, and he said, "What are you doing?" I said, "I can't do it!" You finally convinced me to be scared of it, too; I can't do it. You're going to have to drive us across."

He said, "I can't!" So, I just backed up on the shoulder of the road until we were off the bridge and made the decision to drive through Tampa, which added at least an hour to the trip. After that, I would have to drive with him around Tampa to get to and from Sarasota. Not only that, but once I gave into that fear, it started growing inside me until I was afraid to go over large overpasses (like the ones in Atlanta) and then medium overpasses (like the ones in St. Petersburg). I wasted all kinds of time going past overpasses and getting off at the next exit and then going around the opposite direction, so I could get where I had to go. Finally, I was sick and tired of being afraid and wasting time. So…I called one of my oldest and dearest Christian friends and a counseling mentor. I told her the situation and asked her if she would go with me while I drove back and forth across the Skyway Bridge until I was no longer afraid. She said sure. The next week I picked her up, drove down to the Skyway Bridge, and we prayed together for deliverance from the fear. I opened the windows and turned up the volume on one of my favorite Christian songs (I believe it was Toby Mac) and hit the gas, singing at the top of my lungs. My heart was pounding, and my lungs were moving at warp speed. When I got to the top, I just focused on all the beauty God had made. Once I did that, I could only praise Him! Going down was easy. We went back and forth that day, each time it being a little easier until the fear was gone. Not only that, but the fear of going over all the other overpasses was also gone. I know God taught me a valuable lesson that day…"What we fight, we will conquer, but what we submit to will enslave us."

Doesn't this apply to all areas as well? If you are trying to make progress emotionally, physically, spiritually, and even financially, you don't pull up when you hit a wall. You learn to break down the wall little by little as you begin to conquer habits that are counter-productive to your growth. I am not talking about not having boundaries or limits or not being you. Each one of us should stay true to who we are, but you can't fully become who you are without pushing the "limits of success" that have been spoken over you or even modeled for you. If you have seen under-developed potential, it can be easy to fall into the trap of mediocrity and just accept it as is. No, it's not! If you are never pushed, how do you know how far you can go? This book is meant to unearth the sleeping giant that is inside each one of you. Stop judging yourself based on how you grew up. You are not that girl or boy anymore. Look all that all you have survived. The trauma, defeat, loss, and you are still here! Doesn't that cause you to look up and see your life from a different vantage point? If you made it through all that, you can overcome anything. For my friend, it was a bridge. What is it for you? That one thing you make allowances for that sidelines you in the game of life. While others are passing you by, you are stuck on the shoulder, gripping your steering wheel, too afraid to begin the climb. Are you willing to live the rest of your life in fear of *what if*? To miss out on the opportunities before you because you are afraid of what might happen? To play it safe? Or is there something inside of you that is charged with the possibility of reaching new heights never imagined?

Fear will lie to you and tell you that you can't. Faith will lift you and tell you that you can. What you believe matters, and what you feed yourself grows inside of you. What is winning the weight battle? I am not talking about physical weight but what you believe about yourself. Does the lie that you will always be bound to fear hold more weight than the freedom that Christ died to give you? Is the weight scale tipping toward your victory or defeat? One of the great things about watching sports is the drama that unfolds in a game. Inevitably, there is a point in the game where there is a shift in momentum. A team could be down, but one play can change the flow of the game and even the outcome of the rest of their season. If you're a fan of the team that comes back and wins, it is something that you'll talk about around the dinner table or watch repeated highlights of. Comebacks are memorable. What are you trying to come back from? Is it a debilitating emotional or mental setback? A relationship that has gone bad and now claims the rights to your emotional health? I am not making light of your situation, but we need to clarify something: being hurt is one thing and being tossed out of the game because of something you did is another. You can play hurt and still win. In fact, it is a prerequisite for success. Your ability to handle pain determines your level of promotion. There are certain truths that can only be discovered in the crucible of pain. I don't know of anyone who is not rising in life, who is not bleeding in some area of their life. There have been times in my life (and continue to be) where God has locked me into a situation to teach me some valuable lessons. My willingness to stay on the operating table helped build in me the wings I needed to eventually soar. My surgeries were some of my greatest moments of breakthrough as old remnants of my former self were cut away, revealing my true nature and worth. My facelifts were necessary as they confronted me with the realization of the joker that lay beneath the surface and exposed the little boy who needed to be healed. The great cover-up is the downfall of any true person or society. To think that we can get away with anything and go unnoticed is misguided. There is One who sees and knows it all. His eyes are attentive to our every move. He knows your greatest need is to come into a true understanding of who you are in Him. This is what makes the resurrection so powerful. It shouts that dead things can be raised to life, the power of sin can be broken and no longer do you have to live in fear because the One who has defeated death is alive and holds the keys to death and the grave (see Revelation 1:18). You are invited to this *life* to play free. To change the game and enjoy the benefits of being in a real relationship with a God who knows you. You in?

POSTSCRIPT

Thank you for being part of the journey. The following resources are a great way for you to take your next steps toward freedom:

Emotionally Healthy Spirituality—Peter Scazzero

Emotionally Healthy Leader—Peter Scazzero

ABOUT THE AUTHOR

At the age of nineteen, Richie Sarlo felt called by God to leave university and enter seminary. In the years that followed, he earned a Master of Theology and Doctor of Sacred Studies from Christian Life School of Theology in Columbus, Georgia.

He and his wife, Misty, were married in 2002 and have served in every area of local church ministry, from volunteer to full-time staff. With over twenty years in full-time ministry, Richie has seen Christians consistently held captive to past hurts, wounds, and traumas, ultimately crippling their growth in Christ.

In 2011, he went through a process of allowing the Lord to heal the wounds, hurts, and traumas of his past, and what emerged from that season was his mandate, "To help broken people like myself find healing in Jesus so that they can live physically, emotionally, and spiritually healthy lives."

In 2015, he and Misty felt called to plant a church with the mission of teaching Christians how to live free by allowing the Lord access to every area of their past, present, and future. This church, the Community Chapel, has a motto that states, "We do hard things!"

Along with pastoring in full-time ministry, Richie is a serial entrepreneur and a passionate communicator.

CPSIA information can be obtained
at www.ICGtesting.com
Printed in the USA
BVHW032028310722
643480BV00005B/85

9 781685 568078